AFTERTHOU
of a
WORM
HUNTER

AFTERTHOUGHTS
of a
WORM HUNTER

D.W.T. CROMPTON

Glenstrae Press

First published in 2009 by
Glenstrae Press

A catalogue card for this book is available from the British Library.

The author thanks the following owners or controllers of copyright for
permission to reproduce materials in the text of this book. Allen Press
Publishing Services; CAB International; Facts On File; Harper-
CollinsPublishers; Jared Diamond; Margo Ewart; Methuen & Co; Pearson Education Ltd; Penguin Books Ltd; PFD (www.pdf.co.uk) on behalf
of The Estate of J.B. Priestley; Random House Inc.; Virago Press; World
Health Organization. The author also thanks the staff of publishers who
referred him to guidance about the Fair Use Doctrine and copyright
law. The author has made every reasonable effort to contact copyright
owners or controllers and apologises to those who had not been traced
at the time of going to press, and whose rights have inadvertently not
been acknowledged. Any outstanding permission will be acknowledged
and any inaccuracy corrected in any future reprinting.

ISBN 978-0-9560690-1-6
Typeset in Perpetua by Glenstrae Press
Printed in Great Britain by Cromwell Press Group, Trowbridge

Contents

"But what do we mean by a born naturalist? We mean a man in whom the zeal for observing nature is so uncommonly strong and eminent, that it marks him off from the bulk of mankind. Such a man will pass his life happily in collecting natural knowledge and reasoning upon it, and will ask for nothing, or hardly anything, more.

Men of science will give us knowledge ..... But still it will be knowledge only which they give us; knowledge not put for us into relation with our sense for conduct, our sense for beauty, and touched with emotion by being so put; not thus put for us, and therefore, to the majority of mankind, after a certain while, unsatisfying, wearying."

These words are taken from a lecture given by Matthew Arnold in the USA in 1883. The text of the lecture is to be found in *The Norton Anthology of English Literature*, Volume 2, edited by M.H. Abrams *et al* and published in 1968 in New York by W.W. Norton & Co. Inc.

Foreword

I am always attracted to a book with an interesting title, and what could be more intriguing than *Afterthoughts of a Worm Hunter*. This is a personal story, about one man's determination to do something about a world wide health problem. It has something for everyone. Good stories, good science and a great purpose; to make the world a better place. This is an uplifting book, and one which will bear re-reading and reflection.

But that's not all. The funds raised by the book will go to the University of Glasgow Centre for International Development (GCID) scholarship scheme, routed through the Chancellor's Fund, to fund postgraduate students from developing countries. It thus both engages the reader and encourages more research and personal development. What could be better, and I am delighted to support the book and the project.

Kenneth Calman
Chancellor
The University of Glasgow

Acknowledgements

Worm hunting is not a solitary activity. My thanks are due to friends and colleagues for much help and support. Inmaculada Adames, Marco Albonico, Akwele Annan, Susan Arnold, Samuel Asaolu, Zed Bashoon, Pat Bidinger, Duvy Carrera, Isabel Coombs, Barbara Craig, Glen Dappen, Denis Daumerie, Dirk Engels, Julie Ewald, Michael Fry, Andrew Hall, Thein Hlaing, Mary Hodges, Celia Holland, Mahroof Ismail, Fasli Jalal, Anne Keymer, Michael Latham, Donald Lee, Peter Lockwood, Antonio Montresor, Darwin Murrell, Malden Nesheim, Bruce Newton, Brent Nickol, Zbigniew Pawlowski, VR Parshad, Juan Pablo Pena-Rosas, Stephen Phillips, Lucy Robertson, John Ryley, George Salt, Diva Sanjur, Lorenzo Savioli, Lani Stephenson, Raymond Stoddart, Douglas Taren, Parr Tate, Harriet Torlesse, Carlo Urbani, Mauro Valencia, Keith Vickerman, Eurof Walters, Peter Ward, Peng Weidong and Zhou Xianmin have been the best of collaborators at the bench and in places where people live.

I thank the institutions that underpinned my studies and travels including Sidney Sussex College, the University of Cambridge, Cornell University, the University of Nebraska – Lincoln, the University of Glasgow and the World Health Organization. I thank Patricia Peters, whose secretarial support could not have been bettered, and Geoffrey Martin of Christ's College, Barry Mills of Bolton Metro Library, David Pollock of the University of Glasgow, Sarah Quinn of the Commonwealth War Graves Commission and Charlotte Sturm of the Rockefeller Archive Center for responding to my enquiries.

I also thank Samuel Asaolu, Virginia Crompton, Rosemary and Irvine Delamore, Peter Holmes, Mikal Mast, Malden Nesheim, Marion Nestle and Diva Sanjur who read and improved various drafts. I remain responsible for any remaining errors, mistakes and ambiguities. The Chancellor's Fund of the University of Glasgow has generously financed this venture thanks to the persuasive efforts of John Briggs and Peter Holmes. Kate and Ian Craig of Glenstrae Press deserve my special thanks for applying their expertise to the editing, design and typesetting of the book and for making the arrangements for its production. Above all I thank Effie, my best friend and most understanding and loving companion.

On Becoming a Worm Hunter

"I might compare a parasitologist to an orchid. He requires long and careful nurturing, he develops slowly, and he is himself a parasite in that he is dependent on many other sciences for material aid. But when he comes to flower he is a rare and beautiful object, scientifically speaking, and is usually slow in going to seed. He may not always smell like an orchid, but we can't have everything."

Reproduced with permission from the Presidential Address to the American Society of Parasitologists by Asa C.Chandler (1946), Volume 32 of the Journal of Parasitology, Allen Press Publishing Services.

"My mother is an editoress and my father studies worms", wrote our son at primary school in Cambridge when asked to describe his home life. How true; I am a parasitologist to trade, dealing with worms which thrive in our bodies and those of other animals. I became a worm hunter. Technically, I am a helminthologist since parasitic worms are known as helminths.

Sam Loring excited me about parasitic worms towards the end of my time at Bolton School in the mid-

1950s. I later realised that Sam had known what science is all about. He knew that scientists work to understand real things based on evidence. Sam asked questions. How do tapeworms pass from person to person? How does a tapeworm flourish in the gastrointestinal tract while bathed in the acid, enzymes and detergents needed to digest food? How does a 20-foot long tapeworm live for years in a living chemical engineering plant?

After serving in the King's Own Royal Regiment (Lancaster), I went up to Sidney Sussex College and the University of Cambridge to read Natural Sciences. My father, Arthur Crompton, had been to Sidney before me. He went from Bolton School in 1928 when the town was under a cloud of economic depression. He was an eponymous beneficiary of what Virginia Woolf called 'Arthur's Education Fund' whereby families down the years made great sacrifices to ensure that their sons would have a good education.

At The Molteno Institute in Cambridge, I was encouraged to investigate the interplay between intestinal worm infections and the nutrition of ducks, rats and mice. Studies involving pigs and humans were included later at Cornell University in New York and at the University of Glasgow. Infection with *Ascaris lumbricoides* became of special interest. Millions of poor people in developing countries suffer from *Ascaris* infection. *Ascaris* becomes established when its minute eggs are unknowingly swallowed. The eggs hatch in the small intestine releasing tiny juvenile worms; these travel to the liver and then the lungs before returning to the small intestine via the trachea, throat, oesophagus and stomach. How can we explain the purpose of the hazardous trip the little worms take through the tissues to get back to where they were in the first place? How do any of them dodge our array of protective immune responses? Once back in the gut, the surviving worms grow and mature. Adult females measure about 300mm and adult males about 200mm. Female worms live for about a year and, if inseminated, each produces about 200,000 eggs daily during this time. Their eggs pass from the

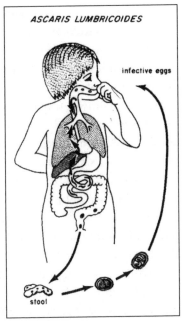

Life cycle of the common roundworm (Ascaris lumbricoides) drawn by Paula DiSanto Bensadoun from Parasites and People by D.W.T.C. and published by Macmillan.

host in stools and the environment becomes contaminated if sanitation and health awareness are inadequate. Some eggs may retain their infectivity for about 15 years. This big white worm will persist until all people have access to affordable and appropriate sanitation. The presence of *Ascaris* in a community is a proxy for poverty.

In children chronic ill health, poor digestion, reduced growth rates, impaired cognitive performance and erratic school attendance accompany infection with *Ascaris*. The infection is particularly severe in communities where the quality and quantity of food are sub-standard. Life-threatening episodes occur when worms become tangled and obstruct the intestine. A single worm may leave its companions and crawl away to block the bile duct or reach the liver and induce an abscess. Other species of worm cause blindness, skin disease, impotency, gross disfigurements, anaemia, cancers and neurological disorders. Humans need to be released from these corrosive and troublesome worms, but we should marvel at their evolution. *Homo sapiens* may be at the top of the evolutionary tree, but *Ascaris* and its fellow travellers have climbed up too, with seemingly little effort.

And so worm hunting involved me with work in China, Dominican Republic, Egypt, Ghana, India, Indonesia, Kenya, Malaysia, Mexico, Myanmar (formerly Burma), Nigeria, Pakistan, Panama, Puerto Rico, Seychelles, Sierra Leone, Tanzania, Thailand and Vietnam. How else would I have seen the pyramids, the Taj Mahal, the Panama Canal, the Forbidden City and a way of life that tourists and holiday makers never see in tropical villages and urban slums?

Scientists record field observations and the results of laboratory experiments. The short essays that follow originated from revisiting my notes. Something I'd written during my travels caught my attention, excited my curiosity and started me thinking about the ups and downs of past and present life in our global village. Places, people and events are real – as is the bit of Lancashire that I could not leave behind.

"I shall therefore here give the anatomy of the Lumbricus teres *that common roundworm which children usually are troubled with."*

From a presentation by Edward Tyson (1683) in which he described what we now know to be *Ascaris lumbricoides,* explained how it reproduced and demonstrated that it is not an earthworm. Volume 13 of *Philosophical Transactions of the Royal Society of London.*

CHAPTER ONE

The Prophet of Doom

"Between Manchester and Bolton the ugliness is so complete that it is almost exhilarating. It challenges you to live there. That is probably the secret of the Lancashire working folk: they have accepted the challenge; they are on active service, and so, like the front-line troops they make a lot of little jokes and sing comic songs."

"Extract" by J.B. Priestley from *English Journey* (© J.B. Priestley) is reproduced by permission of PFD (www.pfd.co.uk) on behalf of The Estate of J.B. Priestley.

On 23 March 1994 I staggered into the Serena Hotel in Faisalabad after an eight hour bus journey from Rawalpindi. I was nearing the end of a lecture tour in Pakistan and the road trip became necessary because domestic flights had been postponed to clear the skies for a military fly-past to celebrate Pakistan Day. The redeeming feature of this hot and tiresome day — the bus was a twenty-four seater Toyota with more passengers than that, loud music and no air-conditioning — was the conversation I had with a local businessman who shared his table with me at the Serena Hotel. He was proud of Faisalabad, then his country's third largest city, which he described as the 'Manchester' of Pakistan.

1

Manchester, encircled by Bolton, Bury, Oldham, Blackburn, Rochdale, Stockport and other towns, had been the heart and soul of Britain's and the world's cotton textiles industry. According to Sir Peter Bell, by 1835 Manchester was without challenge the first and greatest industrial city in the world. The manufacture of cotton goods made Manchester the centre and symbol of industrialization. Manchester's progress gave rise to the proverb "What Manchester says today, the rest of England says tomorrow". I think my new friend's claim for Faisalabad was rather exaggerated, although contemporary statistics showed that Pakistan produced 33.5 million square metres of cotton cloth and 63,000 sewing machines annually.

It started me thinking …. of the rise and fall of the Lancashire cotton industry. My family background was woven into cotton production in Bolton. On my father's side my great grandfather maintained the power supply at Haslam's Mill, my grandmother and great aunts were spinners and my grandfather worked to make textile machinery while my mother's father was a bleacher. Interestingly I had come across Allen Clarke's book, published in 1899, predicting that cotton spinning in Bolton was doomed. At the time Clarke must have been taken for a troublesome agitator because his farsightedness coincided with a period of great prosperity for the mill owners although not for their workforce. Clarke himself had been put to work in the mill as a little piecer when he was eleven in 1874. Such children had the dangerous job of crawling under or even into the spinning machinery to

2

join broken threads. Health and Safety legislation did not exist in his day.

Until Samuel Crompton invented the spinning mule in Bolton, the town had had only one episode of any consequence in British history. During the Civil War, nonconformist Bolton was one of the first places outside London to declare for parliament. This greatly annoyed James Stanley, Earl of Derby, who galloped across from Wigan with some Cavaliers to reverse the decision. He and others like him failed and eventually Prince Rupert with a force of 12,000 soldiers came into Lancashire, the town was overrun and the stubborn defenders were put to death. Later the Earl of Derby was captured and taken back to Bolton for execution.

Cotton spinning and weaving had been cottage industries in and around Bolton for 200 years before Samuel Crompton was born in 1753. The county had a well-established social network of people who knew about cotton. Every day Mrs Crompton insisted that her son spin some yarn and do some quilting. He relied on the household version of a machine which had been built by James Hargreaves one of several inventors and innovators who happened to be Lancastrians. Young Samuel was frustrated by the constant breaking of the yarn and he set himself to design a new machine to reproduce the action of the left arm and finger and thumb of a spinner using a wheel. He worked alone at night for five years to develop what became known as the mule. Music seems to have been Samuel's first love and, having made himself a violin, he played in a theatre orchestra during the day to earn

3

Lancashire street scene before the demise of the textile industry, based on a photograph in the Bolton Evening News.

enough to buy materials and tools to realise his invention. If he had not had to help his mother make economic ends meet, Samuel Crompton might have become the Kennedy of his day.

Crompton's invention gave an enormous boost to the cotton industry. His spinning mule, so called because it was a hybrid of other devices, occupied 48 spindles. By 1825, steam power enabled one mule to manage 600 spindles under the control of one man and two boys. Consequently there was a massive reduction in the cost of production of fine yarn. Abundant coal, plentiful soft water and access to the sea, some 30 miles away by road and soon to be improved by the Manchester ship canal, supported the growth. Access to the sea was crucial. Tonnes of cheap cotton grown in the plantations of America's southern states readily reached Lancashire's cotton mills. New World slavery helped to ensure that the industrial revolution flourished in Britain. Textiles generally accounted for 75 per cent of industrial employment in England in 1840, and cotton textiles accounted for half of this total. The slave plantation had become the principal supplier of cheap raw cotton, a factor that gave Britain's textile producers a massive competitive advantage over rival textile producers, especially those on the Indian subcontinent.

Soon cotton goods from Lancashire made up more than half of Britain's exports. During the 1880s Lancashire textiles were China's second largest import after opium. By 1901, the population of Bolton had grown to 168,000, of whom 58,000 were directly employed in cotton spinning in over 200 mills. Until Crompton's invention, the finest muslin was imported at great cost from India; now it was exported from Bolton. Those who owned the spinning mills, weaving sheds, bleach works, coal mines and engineering works grew rich while thousands of their employees lived in poverty and were deprived of education, health care, recreation and good housing. I wonder if mill owners were bothered by the fact that their wealth was based on slave labour in the Americas and the next thing to slave labour at home. The engineering companies, which made the machinery for cotton spinning, developed a lucrative export trade sending equipment to India, Egypt and elsewhere.

So it was that Allen Clarke attacked the conditions of the cotton industry and foresaw its downfall. He objected to the long hours, to the effects of the hard work on women and their children (born and unborn), to the slipshod factory inspections, to the poor wages and inadequate holidays. Clarke documented the dreadful conditions which prevailed in the cotton mills, the conditions which made a few Lancastrians rich and helped the British economy and empire prosper. Clarke wrote in 1895, "We cannot keep the world's cotton trade for ever"*. He had noted the folly of exporting our machinery. In 1882 Britain exported textile machinery to the value of £7 million and by 1889 the value was £10 million. He wrote, "This is bound to tell a tale, and is telling it now to all who can read with understanding".*

The first cotton spinning mill in Bolton, the St Helena Mill, was opened in 1777 two years before Samuel

St Helena Mill opened for cotton spinning in Bolton in 1777.

Crompton's mule came into full service. Today, virtually nothing is left of cotton in Lancashire. Such mill buildings as have remained have been converted for use as warehouses by mail-order companies or for other purposes. The British textile sector has been hugely affected by overseas competition especially from the Indian sub-continent. In the 19th century, Lancashire ousted the Indian sub-continent from being the supreme centre for textile production; a hundred years later, the sub-continent regained the market. History has turned full circle.

Spare a thought for Samuel Crompton, whose invention perhaps contributed more than that of any other individual before or since to our country's wealth, when he handed over his mule without taking out a proper patent. He would probably have had much more job satisfaction and far wider acclaim in his lifetime if he had stuck to violin making and rivalled, or bettered, the Stradivari family and the craftsmen of Cremona. How many people in Britain today have ever heard of Samuel Crompton?

So Allen Clarke was right; his prophecy of doom for the cotton industry of his native town has been fulfilled. My dinner companion was nearly right; Faisalabad had become a toned-down version of Manchester in Pakistan. Perhaps the switch came about because industrial conditions in Pakistan's textile industry resembled to some extent those in Lancashire's a hundred years ago. If you visit Bolton today you will see the town as a vibrant community with many townsfolk whose roots are to be found in Pakistan. Perhaps they left Faisalabad to avoid cotton spinning.

*Extract written by Clarke in 1895 and reproduced from *The Effects of the Factory System* first published in 1899. London: Grant Richards.

> *"The Industrial Revelation would never have happened but for the wave of great mechanical Inventors, e.g. Arkwright, who invented the Spinning Jenny, or unmarried textile working girl; subsequently, however, this kind of work was done by mules, the discovery of a man called Crompton."*
>
> Reproduced with permission from *1066 and All That* by W.C. Sellar & R.J. Yeatman (1960). London: Methuen & Co.

CHAPTER TWO

On Brazzaville Beach

"What were those few key ingredients that made us human? Since our unique properties appeared so recently and involved so few changes, those properties or at least their precursors must already be present in animals. What are those animal precursors of art and language, of genocide and drug abuse?"

Reproduced with the author's permission (© Jared Diamond) from *The Third Chimpanzee* by Jared Diamond (1992). New York: Harper-Collins*Publishers*.

 Travelling gives time for reading. In William Boyd's novel, *Brazzaville Beach*, Dr Hope Clearwater is reviewing her life. In her words she 'has washed up, you might say, deposited myself like a spar of driftwood'. She arrived in Africa to join scientists based at the Grosso Arvore Research Centre working under the direction of Dr Eugene Mallabar. Research grants, awards, TV documentaries, films — all the trappings of global success — have flowed into the Centre where Dr Mallabar reigns supreme as the authority on the behaviour of chimpanzees (*Pan troglodytes*). This adulation is understandable; chimpanzees are our closest living relatives. Chimpanzee DNA and human DNA are extremely similar and differ by less than two percent. We may ask, should chimps be

known as *Homo troglodytes* or should humans be called *Pan sapiens*?

So why is Dr Clearwater washed up in a reflective mood on an African beach? Her task was to study a breakaway group of chimps in the forests around the Grosso Arvore Research Centre and to her surprise she finds chimps engaged in infanticide, cannibalism and brutal violence as one group sets out to destroy another. Such observations would not do. Dr Mallabar's reputation, built on a book entitled *The Peaceful Primate*, would be on the line. He can accept that chimpanzees hunt, kill and eat other species, but not their own kind. Poor Hope was discredited and driven out.

It started me thinking …. why, despite our extremely close relationship to chimpanzees and gorillas, do we have such an exaggerated capacity to plan and inflict torture, humiliation, cruelty, slavery, mass-murder, warfare, extermination, racism, ethnic cleansing, mutilation and genocide. In recent times we can recall Hitler and the holocaust, Stalin and his purges, Pol Pot and the killing fields, genocide in Rwanda, slaughter and mutilation in Sierra Leone and other examples. Why do we do it, so often on such a massive scale? Is it linked to our capacity, unlike gorillas and chimpanzees, to assemble, store, use and pass on vast amounts of knowledge to the next generation? Is one society desperate to protect its knowledge and restrict its use for itself? Is it because knowledge is power? If we do not exploit our knowledge over others will the tables be turned? Knowledge creates opportunities, opens up resources, develops markets and creates

10

wealth. This proposition may be an extreme over-simplification, but the fact is that two major differences between humans and non-human primates are first, our ability to pass on knowledge from one generation to the next without the help of genes and, secondly, our propensity for cruelty, slaughter and exploitation of fellow human beings.

Field work has shown that some of our primate relatives do have a brutal streak, but sometimes we can interpret their seemingly vicious behaviour as making justifiable evolutionary sense. For example, when a new male gorilla takes charge of a family group he is likely to kill any infants not yet weaned. If an adult female loses an infant before weaning she will come into oestrus much earlier than if still lactating, thereby offering the new dominant male an early opportunity to pass on his genes. In this interpretation, infanticide is seen as part of a functional male reproductive strategy.

Here in Britain and the USA we cannot sit back and be innocent of organized inhumanity. For centuries slavery was rife between kingdoms and communities in Africa and our forefathers exploited its existence. European involvement in the slave trade across the Atlantic Ocean was an atrocity that lasted some 400 years and resulted in over 12 million captives leaving the West African coast for the New World. About 54,000 voyages were made to transport Africans across the ocean; millions died under the awful conditions. Best estimates indicate that over 2.5 million Africans made up the cargoes of British ships during over 12,000 voyages. This episode ranks equal in every way to the crimes of Pol Pot or Hitler. How on earth did humans get involved in doing that to other humans?

My visits to Sierra Leone stimulated my interest in the history of the slave trade. Europeans did not introduce slavery into Africa. David Livingstone's accounts of life in Africa make that perfectly clear. Rather our forefathers exploited what African kings and chiefs did following victory during local feuding. Merchants in major ports such as Bristol, Glasgow and Liverpool simply took advantage of the practice. One prosperous entrepreneur was Richard Oswald, a Glasgow merchant whose business, which depended on the Atlantic Triangle, flourished in the middle of the 18th century. Modern Glasgow is proud of that part of the city centre which is called today 'the Merchant City'. How many modern citizens and visitors know anything about the merchandise and deals on which much of the city's 18th century wealth was founded? In his book *The Slave Trade*, H. Thomas drew attention to Richard Oswald who had property in London, Florida, Jamaica, Virginia and in Scotland, at Auchincruive, where his estate and mansion came to form part of the Scottish Agricultural College. He was a member of a syndicate that owned Bence Island in the estuary of the river that flows into the Atlantic Ocean, by Freetown, Sierra Leone.

In Oswald's time, slaving from Sierra Leone worked as follows. Local chiefs would raid their neighbours and would then hold the captives in stockades, usually on off-shore islands whence escape would be difficult or impossible. In due course, the slaves were exchanged for supplies from Europe and the dreadful transport to market in the New World began. Life on Bence Island must have been cruel and in total defiance of human rights, and it must have been bizarre. Apparently, a golf course was constructed on the island for the benefit and recreation of ships' captains and friends. The caddies were slaves, decked out in kilts made from cloth specially woven for the purpose in Scotland.

Meanwhile in Britain during the early 19th century, Thomas Clarkson, William Wilberforce and others worked tirelessly to rouse public opinion against slavery. On 1st August 1834 celebrations were held in London to mark the first day of the abolition of slavery in the British colonies. The Slavery Abolition Act, which provided for slaves in the colonies to be set free and their owners compensated, had been passed in 1833. Sadly, William Wilberforce died a month before the Act completed its passage through parliament. Some former slaves eventually made their way back to West Africa where Wilberforce is still honoured and commemorated by having a district of Freetown named after him.

Campaigning for the abolition of slavery was also gaining ground in the USA and the nation began to divide into two camps. People in the south insisted on retaining slavery on which their economy depended while most in the north demanded abolition and emancipation. The few supporters in the north were the "lords of the loom" who needed cotton for their business supplied by the "lords of the lash" in the south. Opinion on both sides was influenced and further polarised by the publication of *Uncle Tom's Cabin* by Harriet Beecher Stowe. Harriet was born in Connecticut in 1811 in a deeply religious family in the Calvinist tradition. Later, while living in Ohio, she saw both sides of the slavery conflict first hand. She was appalled by the Fugitive Slave Law which legitimised the return of escaped slaves. Plantation owners from neighbouring Kentucky could pursue slaves who had escaped into Ohio despite the fact that the Law held no sway there. The first impact of her great book was to block enforcement of the Fugitive Slave Law.

Harriet's book appeared as a serial from 5th June 1851 to 1st April 1852 in the *National Era*, a paper which steadfastly campaigned against slavery. John P Jewett of Boston realized that a version in book form would be a best seller and so it was released in two volumes on 20th March 1852. Jewett was right. About 30,000 copies sold during the book's first week, and by the end of the first year over 300 thousand copies had been sold in the USA, one and a half million in Britain and translation into 22 languages had taken place. Such a sales record at that time was phenomenal given the levels of literacy, communication and transport.

Some historians have suggested that *Uncle Tom's Cabin* played a part in starting the American Civil War. In 1862, President Abraham Lincoln is reported as having said to Harriet that she was the little lady who wrote the book that made this Great War. He may not have been elected President without it. Our present circumstances would probably have been very different had the resolution of the war not been in favour of the Union.

Common experience shows that books based on natural science, politics and economics, such as those written by Charles Darwin, Karl Marx and Adam Smith, make a difference to our understanding of human behaviour and activity. Many novels are written for the entertainment and pleasure of their readers; we do not expect them to change the world. The responses of readers to Harriet Beecher Stowe's novel brought about cultural turmoil and supported change in the USA in the 19th century. I may never have thought in any depth about the extent of human cruelty if I had not read William Boyd's novel, *Brazzaville Beach*. Truth may sometimes be stranger than fiction, but fiction may sometimes be more influential than truth.

> "In his work on evolution in the 19th century, Darwin intimated that man must be of African origin, because his closest living relatives, the gorilla and the chimpanzee, are entirely African."
>
> Reproduced from *Cultural Atlas of Africa* edited by Jocelyn Murray. New York: Facts On File.

15

CHAPTER THREE

I Didn't Know
the Territory

*"Culture is about shared patterns of identity, symbolic
meaning, aspiration, and about the relationships between ideas and perspectives, about self respect and a
sense of security, about how individuals are socialized
and values are formed and transmitted."*

From *Through African Eyes: Culture*, chapter 3 in *Our Common Interest*.
Report of the Commission for Africa (2005).
www.commissionforafrica.org

Meredith Willson's Broadway show, *The Music Man*
opens with Charlie the anvil salesman explaining to
passengers on the train to River City, Iowa, that
Harold Hill doesn't know the territory. Harold is a
confidence trickster who manipulates naive farming
people into buying musical instruments they don't want
so that they can establish a boys' band they don't need. The
territory of which Harold is ignorant has psychological
boundaries set by social interplay, attitudes and traditions.
Harold arrives in River City without any knowledge of the
residents or their interests and constructs. He doesn't
care; he is intent on his line of business unconcerned that
his activities give legitimate salesmen a bad name. On leaf-

ing through my travel journals I found I had recorded an episode which clearly showed that I didn't know the territory. I was not in any way a swindler, unlike Harold Hill, quite the reverse, but it started me thinking .... I had set about bringing my version of scientific knowledge to people about whom I knew nothing.

My first visits to Africa were to Machakos District in Kenya where people were habitually infected with the common roundworm. The geographical and administrative names had been assigned by European colonialists who carved up Africa and imposed systems with little regard for the culture and traditions of the indigenous people. I ought to have known I was in Masaku which is part of Ukambani, the homeland of the Akamba people. Machakos is a corruption of Masaku, the name of a revered prophet of the Akamba.

Ukambani lies just south of the equator. There are many small, extinct volcanoes and the climate is hot and often dry. Most rain falls between the end of March and the beginning of June. Several million Akamba live in Ukambani, mainly in the western part, where the soil and water availability support the growing of maize, beans, millet, sorghum, cassava, various fruits and vegetables. Coffee was the main cash crop when I worked there. Apparently, the ancestral Akamba were, in prehistoric times, nomadic pastoralists who have been settled as farmers for hundreds of years on this tropical plateau of Africa.

How I discovered that I didn't know the territory came about as follows. Our investigation in Ukambani concluded with offering free deworming medicine to the local people. There was a great response in the community, especially from the primary school teachers, who persuaded us to arrange an annual programme of free deworming for school-age children in the local villages. This was agreed and the teachers were asked to give the medicine to their pupils. We organised a big gathering to explain about health problems caused by worm infections and about measures to reduce the risk of infection. I found myself lecturing the people on hygiene practices and infectious agents in total ignorance of their background and beliefs - what anthropologists would call the Akamba cosmos or world view. One revered old lady argued that the children should not take our medicine. "Look at their stools," said she, 'it gives them worms!' Now I have benefit of hindsight; then I was quite incensed and started to dish out a large helping of western scientific wisdom. I should have expected that a person with no knowledge of infection processes and only able to see things with the naked eye, was entitled to conclude that our tablets could turn into worms.

I began to behave in a way which has justifiably upset so many Africans. Kivuto Ndeti, a distinguished sociologist from the University of Nairobi, encapsulated the problem when he wrote, "The missionaries, colonial administrators, and 'scholars' of the western world presented Africa and Africans with such arrogance that most of the students felt ashamed of having been born black. Africa was portrayed with disdain and mockery as being full of disease, parasite-ridden, poor, pagan, primitive and savage. The European was projected as the Redeemer who came to civilise and liberate the lowly Africans from the shackles of demons, diseases, poverty, paganism, chronic tribal welfare, ignorance and barbarism. The message was thundered with such authority that any African without the integrity to stick to his rightful heritage felt total evisceration."*

Fortunately I was working with Michael Latham, who did know the territory, and he rescued the situation. I learnt something that day that I have never forgotten. The remit of scientists is to obtain and share knowledge but not to tell people what they must do with it. We can advise if asked. At the time, Michael Latham was Professor of International Nutrition at Cornell University, New York. He was born in Tanzania, qualified in medicine at Trinity College, Dublin, and then became nutritional adviser to the government in Tanzania. Here is how Michael regained control of the discussion and the community's commitment to the roundworm control programme. He told a story to the restless audience that restored trust and respect. I cannot vouch for the originality of Michael's narrative, but it did the trick.

Michael began "One day an expert came from the United Nations Food and Agriculture Organisation (FAO) in Rome to Dar-es-Salaam to promote protein production in the country. The FAO man announced he would begin by surveying fishing methods and catches since he was already near the sea. After all, fish is a valuable source of protein. I was sent as his interpreter because I was fluent in Swahili, of which the expert had no knowledge. At midday, we arrived at a beach by a fishing village near Dar where an old chap was lounging in a most relaxed fashion

20

in the shade of a coconut palm".

"Is he a fisherman?" asked the expert.

"Yes" I replied.

"Splendid" said the expert "ask him if he's been fishing today and how many fish he caught."

A fisherman returning to Pemba Island, Zanzibar, in his canoe made from the trunk of a mango tree.

So we went across the beach to the old man and I introduced us and told him that this famous protein expert from FAO in Rome wanted to know about his work as a fisherman.

"I went fishing this morning and caught four fish" responded the old man.

"If you went fishing this afternoon you could catch more fish" observed the expert.

"What do I want with more fish?" said the fisherman, "Four is enough for me."

"But you could sell the extra fish and buy better hooks and lines" argued the expert.

"That would mean I might catch still more fish" replied the old man.

"Exactly" enthused the expert, warming to his task, "and soon you'd be able to get a better boat with an outboard motor and a large net and catch more fish."

"Whatever would I do with all these more fish I'm catching?" asked the fisherman who was becoming perplexed and showing signs of stress at all this pressure.

"Why, you'd sell them of course and then you could

employ others to take the boat and do the fishing" said the expert.

"And what," said the old man "would I be doing while the others were fishing?"

"You'd be sitting at home taking your ease" beamed the expert.

"Just like I'm doing already" said the old man, visibly relaxing.

This simple story has such a clear message. Experts from one culture should not crash in and tell people from another how to run their lives and leisure. Imagine how Boltonians would have felt if an eager young man from Kenya had turned up and said that men should tell their women to dig their allotments and grow the vegetables.

When we work with people of different cultures and traditions we should not deny their beliefs and so destroy their trust. The fisherman who met the protein expert on the Tanzanian beach was a simple, practical realist, but I

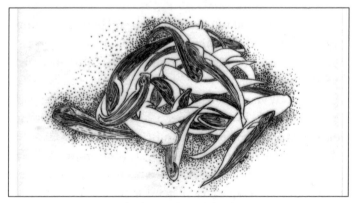

The day's catch on the beach.

expect he had a rich magical and mythical background. Imagine how an unprepared western-trained worm hunter might respond on first hearing the Yoruba explanation of how roundworms (*Ascaris lumbricoides*) came to live in the human gut. Infection with roundworm is common amongst the Yoruba people of Nigeria and their tradition holds that long ago a frightened snake asked a kindly farmer for somewhere to hide from a hungry eagle. The farmer agreed and to be sure of thwarting the eagle he hid the snake in his mouth. After the eagle had gone, the farmer called to the snake that the coast was clear, but the snake had slid down into his gut, which proved to be warm, comfortable and full of food for the treacherous reptile. The snake refused to come out and instead invited his friends and relations to share his new environment. So it came about that the Yoruba got roundworms. Some Yoruba people still decline an invitation to dinner by saying "may the worm in your gut accept my share".

Curious notions about intestinal worms are by no means peculiar to Africa. Until Pasteur's time most Europeans believed that such worms arose by spontaneous generation. German scholars were convinced that tapeworms in the gut were disturbed when organ music was played in church and that they could be expelled from the body by the noise of a Jew's harp. There are recommendations in some of the old medical literature from China to the effect that a physician must be quiet when preparing drugs to expel tapeworms because tapeworms have good acoustic sense and so might be forewarned about what is to happen to them. We may have a lot to learn about tapeworms, but so far there is not a shred of evidence to suggest that they can hear. Incidentally, when Dimitri Tsafendas was tried for the assassination of Dr Hendrik Verwoerd, the architect of apartheid in South Africa and its Prime Minister from 1958 to 1966, he claimed he had been forced to kill Dr Verwoerd by the giant tapeworm in his stomach.

Another set of old Chinese prescriptions claims that roundworms have therapeutic uses, especially for eye diseases. Note this specific remedy for painful ophthalmia. 'Get a large *Ascaris* (roundworm), wash it clean and cut it open at one end. Then drop its body fluid into the affected eye. This treatment will cure even a chronic case of thirty years' duration.' Here is territory with which I do have some familiarity. It so happens that the body fluid of living roundworms contains a stable, potent chemical which kills bacteria. On the face of it, dripping roundworm body fluid into an infected eye might be a smart move, although why anyone should think to do so in the first place is beyond me. There are two major problems with this therapy. First, although roundworms are abundant they would not normally be available unless recently vomited or more commonly passed in someone's stools. So getting a clean, living worm would be tricky. Secondly, much experience has shown that these roundworms release powerful substances which stimulate acute allergic responses in some people. Even after a few weeks of exposure to roundworms in a laboratory not specially equipped for handling worms, some workers can experience alarming bronchospasms, asthma and life-threatening respiratory complications. Roundworms are nasty creatures.

24

Ever since my early safari in Ukambani, I have been wary of telling people how to solve their problems. There is no need for me to get so excited about people like the old lady who claimed that our tablets turned into worms. Her neighbours' experiences convinced them that their children are always happier, livelier and healthier without those unwelcome guests.

*Extract reproduced from *Elements of Akamba Life* by Kivuto Ndeti (© K. Ndeti) 1972. Nairobi: East African Publishing House.

"The world is a book, and those who do not travel read only one page."

Attributed to *St Augustine* and displayed in a Travel Agent's office in Ithaca, New York in 1975.

CHAPTER FOUR

In Itasca State Park

"The small pox, so fatal and so general amongst us, is here entirely harmless by the invention of engrafting, which is the term they give it. There is a set of old women who make it their business to perform the operation every autumn in the month of September when the heat is abated …. the old woman comes with a nut-shell full of matter of the best sort of small pox, and asks what veins you please to have open'd. She immediately rips open … and puts into the vein as much matter as can lie upon the head of her needle."

A procedure from Turkey, described by Lady Mary Wortley Montague in 1717, included in *The Greatest Benefit to Mankind* by Roy Porter (1997) and reproduced with permission. (© Roy Porter). London: HarperCollins*Publishers*.

A benefit for me from my wormy investigations has been accepting invitations to visit universities and share experiences. One year I gave a course of lectures at Nebraska Wesleyan University and studied worms at the University of Nebraska, both in Lincoln, the capital of the Cornhusker State. Americans living along the eastern side of the USA are inclined to make derogatory remarks about Nebraska such as "it's where the East peters out". For me, Nebraska is fascinating with miles of windswept

27

Wind-driven water pump on the great plains of Nebraska.

grass prairie, guarded by sentry-like, wind-driven water pumps, glades of cottonwood trees, and sparse population.

Nebraska is blessed with amazing fossil finds including a recent one now on view to the public at Ashfall State Park. Some 10 million years ago a volcanic eruption discharged vast amounts of ash which were carried east driving all kinds of animals to seek shelter wherever they might. In the spring of 1971, heavy rains eroded the land at a spot in Antelope County to reveal the fossilized skeleton of a baby rhino nestling next to its fossilized mother. These and other animals of the Great Plains, including more rhinos, horses, camels, deer, dogs, elephants, hedgehogs, lizards, peccaries and bats, had died huddled together by a watering hole before the hot ash enveloped them. Excavations have revealed piles of fossilized carcasses; visitors find themselves at Pompeii in the prairies.

In 1982 we drove to Itasca State Park in Northern Minnesota to see the source of the Mississippi River, 2,348 miles north of the Gulf of Mexico. In the park a commemorative plaque reads, "The romantic quest for the source of the Mississippi brought many explorers ... among them Zebulon Pike, Lewis Cass and Giacomo Beltrami to

Northern Minnesota in the early 1800s. The long search came to a close with the discovery of Lake Itasca by Henry Rowe Schoolcraft in 1832 ... the Schoolcraft expedition also collected valuable scientific information, inspected fur posts, vaccinated 2,000 Chippewa against smallpox and negotiated an intertribal peace treaty." It started me thinking .... what sort of man was Henry Schoolcraft who was concerned to bring the life-saving process of vaccination to the local indigenous people? His attitude seemed remarkably different from the conquistadors, soldiers, pilgrims and settlers from Europe who followed Columbus to the New World.

An orthopox virus is the agent of smallpox. The virus is brick-shaped, has a double-strand of DNA and replicates in the cytoplasm of host cells. The virus spreads naturally from person to person when viral particles are inhaled. Thanks to modern vaccination, smallpox has been declared to have been eradicated. The historic date for eradication is 9th December 1979 which represents a triumph first for Edward Jenner and more recently for the Global Commission for the eradication of smallpox. The last case of infection with

Notice in Itasca State Park announcing the discovery of the source of the Mississippi.

naturally occurring wild virus was reported from Merca, Somalia, on 22 October 1977, where Ali Maow Maalin developed smallpox and subsequently recovered. In 1980 the General Assembly of the World Health Organisation formally endorsed the declaration of eradication.

Smallpox was an everyday disease for centuries in Europe. Hardly any family would escape its deadly effects. Estimates show that one in six of those who contracted the disease died, but survivors remained immune. Smallpox was well known in ancient China where the practitioners of traditional medicine would persuade their patients to inhale a powder made from the dried crusts of the smallpox pustules. Physicians in the countries around the Caspian Sea knew that protection from the disease could be obtained by rubbing the thick liquid from a pustule into the scratched skin of a patient. Lady Mary Wortley Montague, who lived in Turkey in the 18th Century, actively promoted this procedure. It became known as variolation and involved the patient's exposure to tissue from a smallpox patient; viruses were unknown at that time. The death rate from smallpox in patients given variolation was reduced to 1 in 60, an improvement of ten times over the death rate from smallpox in unprotected sufferers. Jenner's huge advance was that of using the liquid from cowpox pustules through which he achieved a still better success rate - and so vaccination was introduced. With great conviction and faith in his methods, Jenner carried out his first vaccination trial on young James Phipps in May 1796. Interestingly, it seems that in 1774 an English farmer called Benjamin Jesty had inoculated his wife and two sons with cowpox to protect them against a smallpox outbreak. Nobody would wish to diminish the credit that Jenner has rightly deserved, but perhaps we should make sure that Farmer Jesty's insight is not overlooked. Jesty lived in Dorset and Jenner in Gloucestershire so they would have been unlikely to have met to compare notes, especially since their occupations were so different and since Jesty had his success over 20 years before Jenner.

The impact of smallpox on the Aztec empire shows how devastating the disease was amongst non-Europeans. Diego Velazquez, the Spanish governor of Cuba, sent Hernandez de Cordoba in 1517 and then Juan de Grijalva in 1518 to scout out the territory now known as Mexico. Velazquez got wind of gold and wealth but was wary of being captured, imprisoned, fattened on fine food and then offered as a sacrifice to the gods of the Aztecs. On 18 February 1519, he recruited a more heavily armed force of 530 conquistadors under the command of Hernan Cortes who set sail for Mexico; by the end of the year the Emperor Montezuma (yet to take his revenge!) had been captured. Back in Cuba, Velazquez began to question Cortes' loyalty and in 1520 he sent another force under Panfilo de Narvaez in an unsuccessful attempt to quench Cortes' zeal. One of Narvaez's African slaves had contracted smallpox just before leaving Cuba. Although there is no reason to believe that the conquistadors deliberately introduced smallpox to Mexico, the virus aided the Spaniards in subduing the native population. Some Europeans succumbed to the disease and all feared it, but the native people of North and South America were totally vulnerable. Best estimates indicate that nearly half of the Aztec's eight million subjects were dead from smallpox within six months of the arrival of the infected African slave who accompanied the conquistadors.

A century later and much further north, the Pilgrim Fathers arrived in Massachusetts on 21 December 1620. Smallpox crossed the Atlantic with them and those who followed; within a few years 90% of the indigenous people in the coastal region of New England had been wiped out. Inevitably there was ethnic friction between the European settlers and the indigenous people and again smallpox took its fearsome toll. Apparently the Reverend Increase Mather (1639 – 1723) conducted a special service in Boston and thanked God for the intervention of smallpox during the war of 1676 against the Indians. He is said to have preached "…. but God ended the controversy by sending the smallpox amongst the Indians at Saugust, who were before that time exceeding numerous. Whole towns of them were swept away." Of course, some Europeans died too, but at nothing like the same rate as the immunologically naïve natives.

The Reverend Cotton Mather (1663 – 1728), son of Increase, was another puritan divine who proved to be more enlightened and sympathetic than his father although both were involved in prosecution of the Salem witches. Cotton's roots are to be found in Lancashire. His grandfather was Richard Mather (1596 – 1669) who was born at Lowton, near Winwick. Richard became a school teacher in Liverpool and then, after ordination, had to flee to Massachusetts in 1635 to avoid persecution from the authorities

of the established church. Richard's grandson proved to be
a child prodigy. Cotton was the youngest undergraduate
ever to go to Harvard when he was admitted aged eleven
and he was the first American citizen to be elected to the
Fellowship of the Royal Society of London. On 25th May
1710 Cotton was awarded in absentia the degree of Doc-
torate of Divinity by the University of Glasgow.

Despite his strict puritanical theocracy, Cotton had a
deep interest in science and in 1721 he persuaded his medical friend, Dr Zabdiel Boylston, to introduce Bostonians
to variolation as described by Lady Mary Wortley Montague. Boylston inoculated 247 people, of whom six died,
a far smaller number than would have died had an episode
of smallpox swept through this group. Violent opposition
broke out, Mather's and Boylston's homes were fire
bombed and they were accused of spreading the disease.
Within a few years, however, powerful American advocates
for protection from smallpox by means of variolation included Benjamin Franklin, Thomas Jefferson and George
Washington.

Even worse things then happened in New England
than had occurred elsewhere in the New World. A noto-
rious example was the deliberate introduction of smallpox
to kill North American Indians. In 1763, Sir Jeffery
Amherst, Commander-in-Chief British Forces in North
America, commanded Colonel Henry Bouquet to use
smallpox as a means of breaking up the coalition of Indian
tribes that was gathering to destroy the British garrison.
It is recorded, somewhat incompletely, that Bouquet
replied, "I will try to inoculate....... with some blankets

that may fall into their hands and take care not to get the disease myself." This is one of the best documented historical examples of the practice of germ warfare. Meanwhile, across the ocean that more humane and caring Englishman, Edward Jenner, was embarking on his monumental effort to equip all humanity with protection from this vicious disease.

Was Henry Rowe Schoolcraft trying to redress the attitudes and deeds of Increase Mather, Jeffrey Amherst, Henry Bouquet and like-minded people? From 1967 until the eradication of smallpox was declared, the world had spent USD 300 million on vaccination programmes. Much of this money was earned and provided by the USA, the same country that spent USD 24 billion to get two men to the moon and back. Of course, we are not comparing like with like, but think what WHO could have done with some of that moon money? Our world may not be free from the smallpox virus. It might be preserved somewhere in ice mummies, in tombs yet to be disturbed or in the sealed vaults of power-crazy megalomaniacs. We should be concerned that smallpox virus and other viruses might escape from secret stockpiles of biological weapons. The genomes of orthopox viruses, which infect animals, might mutate and so put humanity at risk once again.

"A virus is a piece of bad news wrapped in a protein."

Quotation by Sir Peter Medawar and reproduced from *Virus X* by Frank Ryan. (©Frank Ryan). London: HarperCollins*Publishers*.

CHAPTER FIVE

The Stool of Oosman Kabbia

"Thou shalt have a place also without the camp, whither thou shalt go forth abroad: and thou shalt have a paddle upon thy weapon; and it shalt be, when thou wilt ease thyself abroad, thou shalt dig therewith, and thou shalt turn back and cover that which cometh from thee."

The fifth book of Moses called *Deuteronomy* 23, vv 12 and 13. King James version (1611).

Years ago in Freetown, Sierra Leone, I was the helminthologist on a pilot study of a suspected association between the educational performance of primary school children and intestinal worm infections. Since then investigations of this proposition have been carried out in Jamaica, Indonesia and elsewhere and evidence is growing to show that a young child's cognitive performance is likely to be hampered by infection with worms. My task was to collect stool samples from the study subjects and then identify and count the worm eggs therein. This procedure gives information about the species of worm present in the host's intestine and the likely num-

35

bers of each species. Put simply, the greater the number of eggs per unit mass of stool the greater the number of worms present.

I am always astonished how co-operative people are in Africa if you ask for stool samples. Knock on any door and ask politely and, without offering anything in return, you will nearly always get a stool sample. People in our society would worry if you went round asking for samples. However, on this particular occasion in Freetown, it seemed that young Oosman Kabbia was having a bit of trouble. His mother asked me to call back later that afternoon. Incidentally, his father was an Imam in the local mosque and that might just have explained why handing over a stool sample had to be complicated. When I returned to Oosman's home, I was given precise instructions as to where the stool sample was to be found. "Make your way towards some banana plants, turn right, cross a small patch of scrub, pass through a very obvious gap in a fence and you will see a bright pink plastic bag on top of a pile of rubbish. Oosman's sample will be in a pot in that bag." So it was.

It started me thinking .... about one of the enormous differences between affluent, industrialised countries like ours, where efficient sanitation carries away the daily stool production of 60 million people, and non-industrialised countries like Oosman's where only 11% of the people have access to improved sanitation. Imagine a situation where only 7 million people in Britain had access to flush toilets and the like. What would we be doing with the vast mass of stools passed every day by the other 53 million people? The lack of sanitation in Sierra Leone contributes significantly to the country's dismal showing in tables of health statistics. Currently in Sierra Leone, life expectancy at birth is 42 years, the infant (under 12 months) mortality rate is 155 out of every 1,000 born alive and the under five mortality rate is 262 out of every 1,000 born alive. These precious children die amongst other things from diarrhoeal disease and problems that would largely disappear if modern sanitation and sewage treatment could be provided.

Our recent forefathers also suffered from the consequences of inadequate sanitation. A dire situation prevailed in the middle of the 19th Century in Bolton which experienced a population explosion when folk settled there to find work as the industrial revolution transformed the cotton textile industry. Bolton at that time had just become a fully fledged borough, Little Bolton and Great Bolton having been amalgamated. Then, as now, Little Bolton encompassed the more expensive housing on the higher ground leading to the Pennines while Great Bolton was the larger portion sprawling south towards Salford and Manchester. In 1848, John Entwisle published a report about the state of public health in the town in response to instructions from the Mayor, Thomas Bridson*. John Entwisle was a local Councillor, a member of the Board of Guardians and Secretary of the Mechanics Institute. His report was inspired and the people of Bolton ought to have erected the biggest statue ever in his honour; it is not too late to do so.

According to Entwisle, the population of Bolton in 1848 was 53,165; numbers had just about trebled since 1801. Two thirds of these folk lived in Great Bolton, worked in the mills and suffered an annual death rate of 3.65%; in other words, 1212 deaths occurred annually amongst the townsfolk in Great Bolton. By comparison, the death rate in Little Bolton was 2.81% meaning that 485 residents died each year. The figures are significantly different and Entwisle's researches revealed further inequalities. The social group he called "gentlemen and persons engaged in professions and their families" had an average age on death of 51 years. These people lived mainly in Little Bolton. The social group he called "operatives and their families" (mill workers) had an average age on death of 19 years and 6 months. The striking difference is largely due to the awful child mortality rate of the very poor people living in Great Bolton. Entwisle reckoned that the infant mortality rate at his time of writing was 278 per thousand live births and the under-five mortality rate was 349 per 1,000 live births (much worse than the poorest countries in modern-day Africa). Overall, he calculated the life expectancy at birth for a mid-19th century Boltonian to be 35 years. At one point he wrote "who can adequately conceive the vast amount of misery indicated by these figures - the agony of acute or prolonged sickness endured by the sufferers, the anguish of bereavement felt by the survivors, the poverty, destitution and pauperism not infrequently resulting from bereavement - the forlorn wretchedness of unprotected orphanage, or solitary widowhood, and all the other domestic and social evils which result from sickness and premature death". Much of what Entwisle had to say about Bolton then could well apply to some of the slums and shanty towns in and around the great cities of sub-Saharan Africa today.

Entwisle went on to identify the causes of this appalling

state of the public health of Bolton's population. Infectious disease amongst the poor was high on his list of causes and he firmly recognised that bad working conditions, bad housing, dirty streets, poor drainage, high population density and inadequate sanitation created the conditions where infection flourished. Entwisle was devastating in his criticism of Bolton's sewerage. He wrote, "the act of Great Bolton empowers the trustees to construct sewers of such magnitude, form and material, as may seem best to them; thus apparently conferring ample powers for the establishment of a complete and efficient system of drainage. But such has been the neglect of the trustees in the management of this important matter, or the defectiveness of the act, that a worse condition of sewerage can scarcely be conceived to exist than that in Great Bolton."

He goes on to describe cesspools, slaughter-house refuse, abominable stenches, people being tormented by thousands of flies, pig sties, middens, dung heaps, liquid filth and heaps of night soil (human faeces). Page after page of Entwisle's report to the Mayor is little more than a catalogue of the repulsive environment in which the poor people of Bolton were expected to survive. In an understatement of all time Entwisle wrote, "cleanliness is conducive to health". He tackled the matter of providing sanitation, noting, "the application of the manure of the towns to the purposes of agriculture has of late begun to occupy the attention of agriculturalists". He presented the Mayor with figures showing how much excreta was produced per person per year and how this could be used to support local agriculture. The scheme depended, however, on the installation of water closets in every dwelling, on a system of pipes and tanks and on hydraulic pumps to move the excreta to where it could be useful.

John Entwisle probably knew little about the microscopic, infectious agents contained in human excrement. Semmelweis, Pasteur, Koch and their followers had not yet put forward the germ theory of disease. Entwisle's interest in using such waste products to support local agriculture would have been extremely dangerous unless the stuff had been allowed to decompose, a process which generates heat, killing the transmission stages of pathogens. For centuries the peasant farmers of China, Korea and other Asian countries have sprayed fresh night soil on their vegetables and crops. The result has been the spread of pathogens into food markets and homes, thus exposing millions of unfortunate folk to infection. A few years ago, the government of the Republic of Korea passed a law prohibiting the use of untreated night soil as an agriculture fertilizer. Almost immediately, the prevalence of roundworm infections (*Ascaris lumbricoides*) began to fall and now that particular parasite is no longer a major threat to public health in Korea. Nevertheless, night soil remains an important resource for poor people, well worth recycling provided it has been rendered safe.

If we leave Bolton in its early Victorian grime and squalor and turn to today's world we find that 58% of the world's population, that is, over 3.5 billion people, lack access to adequate sanitation which would process faeces and urine in a manner to reduce the perils of infectious disease. With knowledge of the amounts of faeces and urine produced by babies, infants, children, adolescents and adults across the age range it is possible to calculate that every day the world's human population discharges over a million tonnes of faeces and even more urine. Something like 80% of this waste material is produced in the developing countries where much of it contaminates the living conditions of millions of people daily. And within this material are the numerous pathogens which spread disease and death. For those of us in the developed world where flush toilets are taken for granted, this situation is hard to comprehend. Before many more years, the world's population may have settled at about 8 billion provided we have managed to halt the HIV/AIDS pandemic. People will continue to defecate and urinate and there are no signs yet that sanitation for humans worldwide is high on anyone's practical agenda. In Britain and elsewhere the development of sanitation has probably been the greatest contribution to public health of all time; everyone ought to be able to benefit from it.

* Extracts from Entwisle's report are reproduced from *A Report of the Sanatory Condition of the Borough of Bolton* by J. Entwisle (1848). London: Simpkin, Marshall and Co.

"But the worst period for sanitary conditions in the industrial regions was the middle of the Nineteenth Century rather than the beginning, because so many of the new houses had by then had time to become slums, since no one repaired or drained them as the years went by."

Reproduced with permission from *English Social History*, second edition, G.M. Trevelyan (1946). London: Pearson Education Ltd.

41

CHAPTER SIX

The Number 8 Bus from Cornavin

"Gorillas are the largest living primates, yet they re-mained unknown to science until 1847."

Reproduced from *Primates*, text by Barbara Sleeper (1997). San Francisco: Chronicle Books.

Bus number 8 stops at Cornavin in the centre of modern Geneva and then climbs steadily to the splendid headquarters of the World Health Organisation looking over Lac Le Mans and away beyond to Mont Blanc and the snow-capped French Alps. En route, the bus passes the League of Nations, the Red Cross and the International Labour Organisation - so by 8.30am it is crammed with secretaries, accountants, experts of all kinds setting off to compile statistics about the problems of the world. When I board a bus in Geneva with its designer-chic passengers I remember the buses in Bolton when I was a boy. Always prominent were notices saying "Spitting Prohibited" presumably as a measure to protect passengers from contracting TB. In the evenings, the buses would be carrying miners with grimy faces because pithead baths were not the norm. Perhaps the most vivid memory is of the bus conductors with their fingers blackened from handling dirty copper coins all day and their habit of calling me "cock".

Once on the bus from Cornavin, I was crushed between two very big men from South Africa; you could think of me being in the middle of the Springboks' front row. They were deep in conversation about a young gorilla which they believed might have contracted polio in a South African Zoo. It started me thinking .... about whether polio was a genuine threat to gorillas. Should we be more concerned about poliomyelitis in gorillas than in children? You might think my fellow passengers had not got their priorities in order. For years, poliomyelitis was a dreaded disease in industrialised and developed countries. My mother sometimes feared that I might end up in an iron lung. The disease is caused by infection with a virus which, on entering through the mouth, eventually settles and replicates in cells of the central nervous system. There is an incubation period of up to 35 days before the initial symptoms arise. Roughly 1% of those who become infected experience cellular changes leading to irreversible paralytic poliomyelitis or even death. President Franklin Delano Roosevelt suffered from polio; his courageous management of this chronic disability probably did much to stimulate Americans to tackle the disease. Some viruses, like those responsible for poliomyelitis, smallpox, measles and yellow fever, are amenable to control and even eradication through immunisation.

In developing countries, many children will normally be exposed to polio virus; transmission is common where modern sanitation is lacking. In the late 1980s some 250,000 children (over 50% of all cases are under three) were estimated to be suffering from paralytic poliomyelitis and perhaps as many as 20 million people of all ages have been crippled as a result of the disease. The worst form of the disease causes death through suffocation when the muscles responsible for breathing become paralysed. This condition led to the development of the 'iron lung', a mechanical device that simulated the muscular rhythms necessary for breathing. Recent figures show that now relatively few cases of poliomyelitis are reported worldwide thanks to a massive immunisation campaign based on a simple, safe and highly effective oral vaccine. Sustaining the progress, however, will require secure and sufficient funds to ensure optimum coverage with the latest vaccines.

The huge effort to overcome poliomyelitis began in 1988 when member states of the World Health Assembly committed themselves to eradicate poliomyelitis by the year 2000. This ambitious eradication plan was seen as an appropriate gift from the 20th to the 21st century. Some excellent progress has been made. In 1996, 400 million children, about two-thirds of the world's children under five, were immunised during mass campaigns against poliomyelitis. During a single day in January 1997, 127 million Indian children were immunised against poliomyelitis. Of course, to aim for eradication is rather ambitious and great difficulties will need to be overcome if the experts are to announce with confidence that cases of poliomyelitis are no longer being detected. Poliomyelitis is still endemic in Afghanistan, India, Nigeria and Pakistan. Unfortunately, the viruses are readily imported into neighbouring countries causing minor outbreaks so constant vigilance is needed to protect populations from the disease. Any action to relieve suffering that depends on mass immunisation and community surveillance is always at risk from war and political unrest.

The effort to eradicate poliomyelitis as a human disease began with the oral poliomyelitis vaccine (OPV) pioneered in 1961 by Albert Sabin and colleagues. New versions of OPV, known as monovalent OPVs, have been developed since. As vaccines go, OPV was cheap and easy to administer; with no additional costs of needles and syringes. Development of OPV, however, provided one of two possible explanations as to how humans might have come to be infected with HIV (human immunodeficiency virus). The possibility of a link between OPV and HIV is a speculative if still plausible hypothesis. HIV is closely related to SIV (simian immunodeficiency virus) and, given the capacity of viral nucleic acid to mutate, there is plausibility in imagining that HIV is derived from SIV. How might humans have become infected? During the development of OPV, the poliomyelitis virus to be used for the vaccine was grown in monkey cells in tissue culture. So, it is just about possible that these cells harboured SIV and that that virus mutated to become HIV, which then contaminated the early batches of OPV. This story may involve much conjecture, but it is pertinent to note that the first cases of HIV leading to AIDS (acquired immunodeficiency syndrome) appear to have occurred in the African countries where OPV was first used.

Under natural conditions, humans are thought to be the only common susceptible hosts of the poliomyelitis virus. Monkeys and other animals can be infected experimentally by means of inoculations with viral suspensions but, despite the concerns of the men on the number 8 bus, it seems to me that gorillas have much more to fear in this world than the polio virus. Gorilla populations are at risk from many factors and unless we take practical measures to protect them they may soon become extinct. At present, varieties of gorilla live in equatorial Western Africa (Angola, Cameroon, Central African Republic, Congo, Equatorial Guinea, Gabon and Nigeria), in lowland eastern Central Africa (Democratic Republic of Congo) and in mountainous eastern Central Africa (Rwanda and Uganda). A subspecies of gorilla is associated with each region; there are estimated to be 111,500 western gorillas, 10,500 lowland gorillas and as few as 600 mountain gorillas. With an overall population of 122,600 animals, all gorillas are threatened and vulnerable; the mountain gorilla is clearly at risk of extinction. Even if more groups of gorillas are discovered the threat of extinction will remain.

A major danger for gorilla populations is habitat destruction driven by internal poverty and external affluence. Forests where gorillas have prospered for generations are cleared for timber and to make way for agricultural crops. During the course of evolution, gorillas have become adapted to life in the forest. They eat vast quantities of vegetable matter including leaves, fruit, roots and bark. They live in family groups, usually dominated by a single male. Maturity is reached after six to eight years. Each successful pregnancy, which lasts for nine months, produces one infant and the normal life span is around twenty-five to thirty years. There is apparently a high rate of infant mortality and, despite the dedicated care provided by the female gorilla, rarely is more than one infant per mother successfully reared during a seven year period. This form of life cycle and rate of reproductive success cannot withstand the contemporary rate of deforestation and habitat destruction.

Hunting for food and the rapidly expanding trade in bushmeat now represents the other main threat to the survival of gorillas and other species of non-human primate. For centuries, forest dwellers have hunted and eaten the animals of their forests and certain dishes have become engrained in the culture. Bushmeat is believed by some to convey special attributes. Eating gorilla makes you strong like a gorilla. Eating chimp makes you cunning like a chimp. We might argue that eating them is bordering on cannibalism given the closeness of their relationship to us. A devastating trade in bushmeat has developed through improved access to the forests and the migration of rural people to the big cities. The migrants may have abandoned subsistence farming as a way of life, but they have not forgotten their traditional taste for bushmeat. Experts estimate that the value of the annual trade in bushmeat - the carcasses of forest animals including gorillas - is worth USD 900 million annually. This annual trade in Ivory Coast is said to be worth USD 117 million, in Gabon USD 100 million and in Liberia USD 24 million. About one

48

tonne of bushmeat arrives every day in the markets of Yaounde, the capital of Gabon. Bushmeat even arrives in western restaurants seeking to cater for the tastes of expatriate African diners.

Poaching for complementary medicinal purposes represents another threat to the survival of gorillas. Poachers will deliberately kill gorillas in order to sell body parts for special curative or protective purposes. For example, in Cameroon a woman may believe that her unborn child will grow to be vigorous and healthy if a gorilla's digit is tied to her hip during pregnancy.

Gorilla numbers are too low to stand any more losses other than by natural causes; vigorous protection is required. Reduction of the demand for bushmeat through education might help. Authorities in Africa will have to decide what to do. There is confusion about which animals can be taken for food and which cannot. Gorillas are protected, but how can enforcement be achieved in such difficult and extensive terrain by governments so short of resources? It has recently been reported that coltan miners in the Democratic Republic of Congo have already eaten many of the gorillas that appeared in the film *Gorillas in the Mist*. Coltan is in great demand for making the tiny capacitors used in mobile phones. Surely some other form of meat can be provided for the miners?

Our destruction of non-human primate species may yet be found to involve a dreadful consequence. Millions of Africans and others are doomed through infection with HIV. The second explanation for the origin of HIV infections in humans is linked to the desire to eat non-human

49

primates. Crude butchery of freshly killed monkeys is bound to have exposed the unprotected hunters to monkey blood. Any such monkeys infected with SIV might well have been the source of what has become HIV in humans. Molecular evidence now seems to suggest that the bushmeat explanation is more credible than that concerned with the development of the polio vaccine.

> *"It happens. Will it go on? —*
> *My mind a rock,*
> *No fingers to grip, no tongue,*
> *My God the iron lung."*

Reproduced from *Paralytic* by Sylvia Plath (1963) in *The Faber Book of Fevers and Frets*, edited by D.J. Enright London: Faber and Faber Ltd.

CHAPTER SEVEN

Anemones are my Favourite Flowers

"As you turn these pages, remember the importance of sight."

Reproduced with permission from the World Health Organization from *Success in Africa: the Onchocerciasis Control Programme in West Africa* text by Helen Bynum (2002). Geneva: World Health Organization.

Blindness devastates and knowledge of impending blindness is frightening. For reasons still unexplained, I developed cataracts in both eyes when relatively young, fortunately in series rather than in parallel. I had a lens implant in the eye which had become useless. Until then I could do no more with that eye than distinguish between daylight and darkness. The other eye was rapidly deteriorating. When the dressing was taken off after the first operation I looked round and saw by my bed a posy of fresh anemones from my mother. The colours were astonishing - quite breathtaking. Every time I see an anemone I have a happy reminder of the restoration of my sight. Later the other eye was successfully treated and I have enjoyed excellent vision ever since.

One day, some 15 years later, I visited a focus of river

blindness up country from Freetown in Sierra Leone. The scene was deeply moving, blind men were feeling their way with sticks or being led along by children. It started me thinking .... about the extent of blindness, its causes, about those who suffer from it, about what needs to be done and whether it ever will be done.

River blindness is a disease which has destroyed the health, eyesight and agriculture of village people in tropical West Africa. The disease depends on the presence of microscopic larvae of a threadlike worm called *Onchocerca volvulus*. Adult worms lodge in nodules about the size of a walnut just under the skin, usually where bone comes near the body surface, such as over the skull. After mating, female worms release thousands of larvae which move into the skin to be picked up by biting black flies. While in the skin, the larvae cause damage and intense itching. Further development takes place inside the black flies which, when they feed again, transmit the worms to another person. Some of the larvae wander out of the skin and invade the eyes, inducing inflammation, and other lesions, leading to visual impairment and then blindness. Men around the age of 40 seem to be worst affected. The disease is called river blindness because the black flies breed in fresh water. For centuries rural people in West Africa have known that poor eyesight predominates in villagers living near rivers. Communities risked famine to avoid blindness by packing up and leaving the fertile land near the rivers. West Africa became littered with abandoned villages.

In 1974 support was mobilised for a massive public health programme designed to deal with river blindness in West Africa. This multinational intervention became known as the OCP, the acronym for the Onchocerciasis Control Programme in West Africa. Efforts began to kill black flies by spraying their breeding sites with insecticides, to kill the larvae by giving people regular doses of a safe drug and to extract the adult worms by surgical removal of the nodules. There is still no drug which disposes of the adult worms in the nodules and, since these worms live for about fifteen years, the OCP

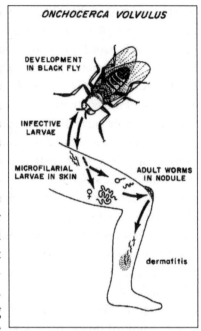

Life cycle of Onchocerca volvulus *drawn by Paula DiSanto Bensadoun from* Parasites and People *by D.W.T.C. and published by Macmillan.*

needed to continue for many years. Surgery was not widely available and was not as cost-effective and quick as a single oral dose of the larvicidal drug. Many people in need of treatment lived in remote and difficult terrain; many black fly breeding sites were sheltered and inaccessible, while civil wars and political upheavals threatened to turn back the clock on progress. Nevertheless, overall in West Africa, the number of cases of blindness fell from

53

35,000 in 1970 to 29,000 in 1995 during the first 21 years of the programme. That was real progress in the context of extremely rapid population growth; the blindness rate had dropped from 0.1% to 0.05% of the population. The OCP ended in 2002 having left behind a major part of West Africa freed from the scourge of river blindness. People in other parts of Africa still need treatment and vigilant surveillance should continue in West Africa if such good progress is to be sustained.

Loa loa, although not as common as *Onchocerca*, is another parasitic worm that may affect the eyes of people in West Africa. Adult *Loa* have a tendency to wander in the tissues and sometimes a worm may crawl through the conjunctiva of the eye. This happening will worry the sufferer, is shocking to behold and may last from a few minutes to a few days. We understand that the worm can easily be removed from the eye with a curved surgical needle and a steady hand following local anaesthesia.

There are more than sixty definitions of blindness. I subscribe to the version which states that blindness is the inability to count fingers at a distance of three metres. That was my condition and, by the time of my first surgery, I doubt if I could have counted fingers as near as one metre. Currently, by the three metres definition, there are at least thirty-five million blind people in the world and a further one hundred and ten million with poor vision. Helminthologists have been justified in seeking to control river blindness, but it may not compare with the public health problem of blindness due to cataract (42% of cases), trachoma (16%) and glaucoma (14%). River blindness accounts for about 1% of the world's blindness cases and a miscellany of factors are responsible for all the other cases. Most blindness occurs in people aged 60 or over, particularly if they live in developing countries. Fifty-eight percent of the world's blind are aged 60 or over and over 80% of these cases are citizens of developing countries.

Cataract is a detectable opacity of the crystalline lens of the eye stopping light rays from reaching the retina. The condition is most common in India (32% of cases), then in sub-Saharan African (20%) and least common in industrialised countries (0.5%). The problem is so common in India that many people believe it to be an expected consequence of growing old. There are numerous causes of cataract ranging from metabolic disorders to rather bizarre conditions. Glass blowers may develop cataracts from over-exposure to infra-red radiation, babies may be born with cataracts due to congenital problems and even lightning strikes may cause cataracts if victims survive.

Cataract is an easily cured form of blindness provided resources are readily available. There are two standard treatments. One is to remove the crystalline lens, an operation taking less than 20 minutes, and provide spectacles. The second is to implant an artificial lens after the defective lens has been removed and again provide accurately prescribed spectacles to work with the implant. For most sufferers, simple lens removal is the obvious procedure, but the millions in need of treatment live where ophthalmologists, equipment and facilities are scarce. Bangladesh has more than its share of blindness due to cataract. Most afflicted people live in villages while the few qualified ophthalmologists live and work flat out in the cities. Cataract statistics have recently been published for neighbouring India, where about 9 million people are known to be blind due to cataract and many more have impaired vision. There are nearly 9,000 qualified ophthalmologists in India, roughly one for every 100,000 people. Even though cataract surgery is well established in India, the need for more health professionals remains; poverty, rural inaccessibility and the poor literacy rate underpin cataract persistence.

Trachoma occurs where hot, dry and dusty climates prevail. The disease is caused by infection with a microbe called *Chlamydia trachomatis,* one form of which may move randomly from person to person where hygienic conditions are poor, while another form may be transmitted during sexual behaviour. Chlamydias are tiny bacteria-like organisms which can live inside the cells of the eye. Their presence results in severe inflammation and conjunctivitis leading to the scarring of the cornea and eventual blindness. Concurrent infections with various bacteria can aggravate the condition. Sometimes the eyelids become deformed and the eyelashes grow inwards to complicate the lesion. Chlamydias were once thought to be viruses, but this view has been corrected and it is known that regular treatment with long-acting antibiotics will eliminate the infection and prevent blindness. Facial cleanliness is an important preventive measure; trials in Tanzania have shown that this simple measure helps to reduce the prevalence of trachoma in children. Face-washing requires either clean water from a safe supply or enough health awareness amongst care givers to convince them that water from other sources must first be boiled. In many parts of sub-Saharan Africa, clean water is not available. Water is too precious for such washing, health education is lacking and fuel is either in short supply or too expensive for the luxury of boiling water before washing.

Glaucoma is the third major cause of blindness, again more common in developing countries than elsewhere. China and India have the highest prevalence of the disease, 42% of all cases between them, while sub-Saharan Africa is afflicted yet again, this time with 17% of the cases. Glaucoma is impairment of the optic nerve caused by increased hydrostatic pressure inside the eyeball. In our industrialised society, the onset of glaucoma can be detected quite easily through regular visits to opticians, who are able to measure upward changes in eyeball pressure. That diagnosis can be followed by drugs to relieve symptoms and help manage the condition. Some drugs now act to reduce the pressure. In developing countries the lack of medical equipment, the shortage of trained personnel, the remoteness of the population, problems of travel and the high cost of drugs ensure that glaucoma persists.

Vitamin A deficiency can also lead to blindness. Children between the ages of six months to three years are most at risk and over 300,000 in developing countries are probably blinded or debilitated every year because they do not get enough vitamin A in their food. Vitamin A is also known as retinol, a clear indication of its importance to eyesight. The vitamin is found in foods of animal origin; most families in developing countries are vegetarians, of

Sculpture by R.T. Wallen in front of the headquarters of the World Health Organization, standing as testimony to the public health endeavour to overcome river blindness in West Africa.

necessity rather than choice. Animals are too precious to be eaten for food. Some plants, including carrots, tomatoes, sweet potatoes, mangoes and red plums, are rich in β-carotene which the body is able to convert to vitamin A. It is something of a mystery that vitamin A deficiency can be found in children living where juicy mangoes abound for at least part of the year. Tackling the problem at the family level involves good nutritional education to encourage as varied a diet as possible and include orange-coloured fruits and vegetables as the seasons allow. In the community, dietary supplementation is sometimes achieved by adding the vitamin to sugar or by providing vitamin A capsules through clinics. Good compliance, again based on good education, is needed for these measures to have an impact. In the future, genetic manipulation may enable scientists to develop staple foods which actually contain vitamin A.

So, will the world respond to the scale of blindness, almost all of which is now preventable? Major sources of blindness could be brought under control quite rapidly, given political will and resources. By accident of birth, I lived where eyesight could be restored granting me a happy and productive career. By other accidents of birth nearly 35 million people are blind and another 110 million have problems with vision because they live where care is lacking or too expensive. Their quality of life, their productivity and their enjoyment of the world is diminished. They cannot rejoice over anemones. Perhaps of all the world's health problems, blindness deserves the top priority because much of it can be cured or prevented - and an anemone could be the symbol to inspire the effort.

> *"I once was lost, but now I'm found, was blind,*
> *but now I see."*

Reproduced from *Amazing Grace* by John Newton (1779) sometime master of the slave ship *Greyhound*. In *Combined Sound of Living Waters-Fresh Sounds* compiled by Betty Pulkingham and Jeanne Harper (1978). London: Hodder and Stoughton.

CHAPTER EIGHT

A Cut Above the Rest

"The story of the sanitation of the Canal Zone consti-
tutes one of the most dramatic examples that the world
affords of what medical science can accomplish when
properly backed by government."

Reproduced from *History of the Panama Canal* by Ira E. Bennett (1915)
Washington DC: Historical Publishing Company.

My family attended Fletcher Street Methodist
Chapel in Bolton. For some years after the end of
the Second World War, the chapel held its annual
Sermons with an important Methodist as the
preacher. The event usually began with an early
morning procession of witness by the faithful led by the
buglers and drummers of the Boys' Brigade. I went once
and I think we marched round the local Roman Catholic
Church and then retired to hear exhortations about being
good Methodists. A stalwart of the Boys' Brigade told me,
almost breathless with excitement, that the company was
going camping - "t'other side o't' cut" near Adlington.

They were to pitch their tents, dig their latrines, light
their fires and blow their bugles on the other side of a section of the Leeds-Liverpool canal system or the Liverpool-
Leeds canal, depending on whether one was born on the
east or west side of the Pennines. Cuts are canals. Years

Bridge over the Leeds-Liverpool canal near Adlington.

later, thousands of miles from home, I saw the magnificent Panama Canal for the first time. It started me thinking .... about canals and, particularly about the Panama Canal. The construction and ultimate success of the canal as a commercial venture had depended not only on engineers but also on the forefathers of my profession. I was standing where the great Dr William Crawford Gorgas had plied his trade. The disciplined public health procedures introduced by Gorgas enabled the canal to be completed and opened in 1914 despite endemic yellow fever, dysentery, malaria, typhoid, and the assemblage of diseases that had destroyed the French effort. The canal extends for 82 km, connecting the Pacific and Atlantic oceans, reducing the natural sea journey from San Francisco to New York by about 12,500 km. The *Queen Elizabeth II* paid a toll of nearly USD 90,000 to sail through the canal in 1980, while

Richard Halliburton paid 36 cents to swim through the canal in 1928.

In Europe, canal construction began in earnest in the second half of the 18th century when they became the navigation arteries of the expanding industrial revolution. At one time the civil engineers James Brindley and Thomas Telford were reckoned to have built 6,800 km of these supply and distribution lines in Britain. Brindley was highly innovative, using tunnels and aqueducts rather than locks to get round obstacles. His Bridgewater Canal, built to move tons of coal from the Duke of Bridgewater's mines at Worsley to nearby Manchester, is an outstanding example of Brindley's craft. G.M. Trevelyan in his *English Social History* showed how important he thought the construction of the Bridgewater Canal was to the progress of the industrial revolution. The inside cover of this monumental book is a map of the counties of England in which the village of Worsley features on an even footing with Manchester, Birmingham and the country's major cities.

The Forth and Clyde Canal in Scotland, linking two estuaries from Grangemouth to Bowling over a distance of 56 km and requiring 40 locks, has been renovated to extend its leisure use. The dimensions of its locks determined the size of the boats. Scotland's famous Clyde puffers, immortalised by Neil Munro with the *Vital Spark*, were built and launched at places like Maryhill and Kirkintilloch on the canal itself, with the size of the locks again determining the size of the puffers. The same principle applied later to the Panama Canal. Shipbuilders worldwide designed and launched vessels big enough to fill a lock to capacity. Even today, many modern container ships are able to negotiate the Panama Canal.

The possibility of a waterway through the isthmus between the Americas was first discussed in 1524 by the Spanish colonists, but it was not until the Suez Canal had been completed in 1869 that attention was paid to the views of Ferdinand de Lesseps who had masterminded the project for France. The construction of the Suez Canal had been helped by the fact that earlier on, around 2,000 BC, ancient Egyptians had linked the Mediterranean Sea to the Indian Ocean along the same route followed by de Lesseps' engineers. Ferdinand de Lesseps was an entrepreneur, fund-raiser and salesman par excellence, the archetypal venture capitalist. He formed the Interoceanic Panama Canal Company and invited fellow countrymen to invest. He announced that the canal could be built from Panama City to Colon in eight years at a cost of USD 50 million and he dangled before his shareholders the prospect of handsome dividends from the dues to be paid by the shipping using the canal. Work began in 1881 and stopped in 1889 when de Lesseps' company was declared bankrupt having already spent USD 300 million and having left many French shareholders in financial ruin. Worse than that, however, was the disastrous loss of life. Over the period of the attempt to build the Panama Canal, French personnel managers imported over 100,000 labourers, mainly from Jamaica. At least 22,000 of these are known to have died on site, mainly from yellow fever or malaria. Typhoid fever, smallpox, pneumonia, dysentery, heat-stroke, snake bite and malnutrition were other common causes of death. The French authorities cared for the sick and built hospitals, but these were little more than elegant death traps and, according to Gorgas, "If the French had been trying to propagate yellow fever they could not have unwittingly provided conditions better adapted for the purpose".

During this time, Panama was part of Colombia and Panamanians wanted their independence. A revolutionary junta declared Panama independent in November 1903. The Colombian government despatched troops to quell the rebellion and the USA despatched battleships to prevent their landing. Then the USA recognised the independence of Panama and took over the treaty signed between

Thatcher Bridge carrying the Pan American Highway over the Panama Canal near Panama City.

Colombia and France regarding the canal, its construction and financial future, should it ever be completed. Starting in 1904 the Americans steadily worked at the construction and a decade later on 15 August 1914, the USS *Ancon* became the first ship to sail from the Pacific to the Atlantic Ocean. The US government took control of the canal and the Canal Zone and over the years earned huge revenues compared with the initial investment. In 1977 US President Jimmy Carter and Panama President Omar Torrijos agreed that the canal should revert to Panama at the end of 1999. That has come about, with the USA retaining responsibility for the defence of this engineering masterpiece.

Much of the credit for this success must go to the skills and planning of the American military engineers who got the job done, particularly to Colonel David Galliard after whom the Galliard Cut is named. This cut has banks over 3000 feet in height and marks the canal's passage through the continental divide. The overall cost of the job was USD 375 million. For most tourists and no doubt many others, the contribution of Dr Gorgas gets overlooked. While working in Cuba, Gorgas had proved to his own satisfaction that mosquitoes had to be responsible for the transmission of the agent of yellow fever and he would have been well aware of their involvement in malaria since Ronald Ross had recently discovered that malaria parasites were transmitted by female mosquitoes.

Gorgas was put in charge of the health of the American labour force and he had to overcome considerable scepticism and opposition before he was allowed to tackle the deadly diseases that had shattered the French effort. Gorgas introduced measures, punishable if ignored, to drain swamps, cover exposed water supplies, spray oil onto open water and fumigate houses. Without the aid of vaccines or modern prophylactic and curative drugs, he reduced the earlier mortality rates from yellow fever and malaria by the decimation of mosquito populations. He introduced screens for doors and windows and set up quarantine procedures, so protecting uninfected people from mosquito bites. By 1907, yellow fever had been eradicated from the isthmus.

Malaria proved to be as formidable problem as yellow fever. Besides his blitz on mosquitoes and their breeding sites, Gorgas resorted to the widespread use of quinine. He set up dispensaries where workers went to get daily lemonade containing quinine; the bitter taste was disguised by the lemons. Quinine use reached the staggering total of 8.7 million doses during one year using 1,300 kg of the drug. The successes of Gorgas's measures speak for themselves. The annual death rate in Panama City when the canal was nearing completion was 25 per 1000 compared with a death rate of 23 per 1000 in London, 28 in Moscow, 38 in Cairo and 55 in Bombay. Public health workers today can still learn much from the pioneering work of Gorgas. He should join the ranks of Jenner, Semmelweis, Pasteur, Koch, Metchnikov, Manson and Fleming whose efforts transformed our knowledge of infectious disease.

Ferdinand de Lesseps was not the first to think of digging the Panama Canal. In 1698 a group of 1,200 Scottish adventurers arrived at San Blas in Panama at a peninsula now called Punta Escoces where they built Fort St Andrew and called the place New Edinburgh. The purpose of this venture was to find gold. In one of their reports they recorded "The country of Darien is one of the most famous Isthmus's in the world. If it were possible to cut a channel from sea to sea, capable of shipping, it would facilitate the navigation of the world ..., but it's next to an impossibility...". Tropical disease rapidly struck and by April 1699, 200 had died. Spanish settlers resented the Scots and put them under siege. The enfeebled survivors left and eventually about 500 reached Jamaica and New York. Two further Scottish expeditions went out to San Blas during 1699 to try and establish a colony and make a fortune, but their efforts also failed. In 1979 the Panamanian government allowed a team of archaeologists to explore the site of New Edinburgh. Plenty of evidence of the Scottish presence was found although there were no old bagpipes.

There is yet another twist to this tale — another side o 't' cut! A friend told me that a Scottish engineer called Fleming Brown was also keenly interested in developing a waterway between the two great oceans. In 1897 he proposed to dig a tunnel through a mountainous region at San Blas. The tunnel was to be straight, 100 feet wide with a height of 170 feet, so providing a water depth of 34 feet and allowing 136 feet for masts. Fleming Brown's plan was costed and compared with the costs of building such tunnels as that at St Gotthard connecting Italy and Switzerland which had been finished in 1872. His tunnel would cost £320 per yard and £17.5 million overall. He worked out the number of ships that could pass through per hour

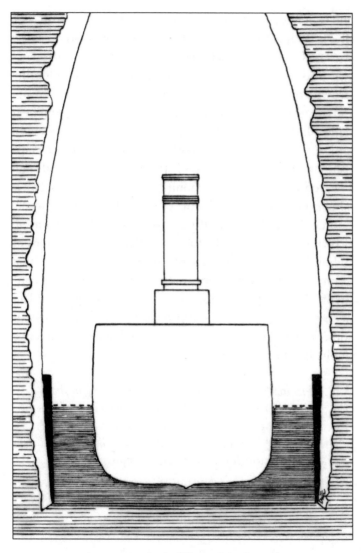

A cross section sketch of Fleming Brown's tunnel.

and estimated that at a speed of 4 mph, 124 ships, a quarter of a mile apart, could be in the tunnel going from east to west or *vice versa* over a fourteen hour period. Hydroelectric power would be used to light the tunnel. Fleming Brown argued that the costs of all the locks and reservoirs, the traction systems for moving ships and all the paraphernalia planned for the canal between Panama City and Colon would be avoided with his tunnel. Today's ships using the canal are raised 85 feet above sea level and then lowered again. All this planning was underway in 1897. The French effort had not yet failed but was clearly doomed. The Foreign Office was consulted and Fleming Brown was advised on 13 July 1897 that the exclusive right to build the waterway belonged to the Interoceanic Canal Company in collaboration with the Colombian government. He had to abandon his plan. Even if approval had been given, the task would probably have failed without somebody with Gorgas's genius for implementing effective public health measures.

> *"William Gorgas, who headed the [US] Army medical services in the FirstWorldWar, died of a stroke while in London in 1920. Before his death, Gorgas was visited in hospital by King George and was knighted for 'the great work which you have done for humanity'."*
>
> Reproduced from *The Path Between the Seas* by David McCullough (1997). (© David McCullough). NewYork: Simon & Schuster.

CHAPTER NINE

Yorubaland

"Nigeria is named for the river Niger, which means black, and there is no place else in Africa quite like it. The contrasts are greater, the beat is faster, the dreams bigger. Every time I entered Lagos, the capital that seems a combination of Calcutta and Harlem, I shuddered, wondering if there wasn't an easier way to earn a living than journalism; every time I left I felt exhilarated, my belief in Africa's future rejuvenated, for I knew that I had been in the most exciting country in all of the Third World."

Reproduced from *The Africans* by David Lamb (1985). (© David Lamb). London: Methuen Ltd.

Victorian Britain was captivated by tales of the intrepid men and women who set out to bring light into Darkest Africa, who went forth to "civilise the natives". Scrutiny of fossil bones and molecular analysis of DNA, however, tells us that Africa's principal contribution to our world has been humanity itself. Civilisation began there. Our species emerged some 400,000 years ago in Africa and spread out from its eastern region to colonise the continent and people the world. We are all Africans. We must assume that the Victorians were not thinking of electromagnetic waves when they discussed light and dark in an African context. The sunshine there is quite exquisite and the beautiful darkness of night is truly described by Dylan Thomas's 'bible black'.

That Victorian notion of Darkest Africa is readily dispelled at Ile-Ife, the cradle of the Yoruba civilisation. With colleagues from Obafemi Awolowo University, Ile-Ife, and Trinity College, Dublin, I helped to investigate the proposition that children are in some way predisposed to harbour a particular number of roundworms. Participants in the study were offered deworming medicine, all the stools passed during two days were collected and then the number of worms expelled from each child was counted. This is not a pleasant task in a hot and humid place. The procedure was repeated at six-monthly intervals. A pattern emerged from all these worm counts; the same children were consistently found to have many worms, the same had moderate numbers of worms, the same had few worms and the same had none. Here was statistical evidence of some form of predisposition to worm burden, especially since the children in the study were equally exposed to infective stages. The families who took part in this study of predisposition to worm burden were Yorubas. It started me thinking …. who are the Yorubas, how did they come to form such a major part of modern Nigeria, and who was Obafemi Awolowo?

Nigeria is a recent nation state created and acquired by Britain towards the end of the 19th century, when the governments of France, Britain, Germany, Belgium and Portugal shared out the territory of the African continent for economic purposes. Britain's formal, imposed control of Nigeria was remarkably brief; the country gained full independence in 1960 and adopted the status of a republic in 1963. Political disputes have featured in Nigerian life ever since, but this is hardly surprising given the manner in which the country came into existence. The territory of the Yoruba was split, with eastern Yorubaland forming a major portion of Britain's Nigeria. Obafemi Awolowo, more of him later, at one time appeared to question whether being identified as 'Nigerian' meant anything more than living within the boundaries of the country called Nigeria. He suggested then that being 'Nigerian' did not convey the same sense of nationhood as being 'English' or being 'French'.

Yorubaland was or is situated between the River Mono in the west and the River Niger in the east. The people of this part of Africa did not come to be known as Yorubas until the 19th century. Previously they were known by the names of the groups to which they belonged, such as Oyo, Egba, Ekiti, Ijesa and Ijebu, but they shared the same language and enjoyed common traditions. By the year AD 1000 the various groups of people in the region had become better organised and a form of government was set up in Ile-Ife by a powerful and mysterious man called Oduduwa. Perhaps we might compare the Yoruba legends of Ile-Ife and Oduduwa with those of Camelot and King Arthur, although there is absolutely no question that Oduduwa was real and that Ile-Ife is a thriving city.

Archaeologists reckon that people reached this part of Africa some 17000 years ago. Yams were being grown and artistic work was established. I single out yams because my Yoruba friends delight in them and respect their powers. For example, in an anthology compiled by Chinweizu we read, "To plant yam is costly - but it amply repays its own debt. You put the yam to bed in the ground it will

73

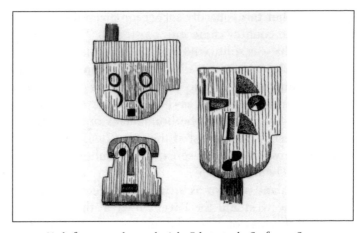

*Masks from a metal screen by Agbo Folarin in the Conference Centre
at Obafemi Awolowo University.*

bring you money that will plant you on top of a beautiful woman"*. Linguistic work has not contradicted the findings of the archaeologists; all the main groups, including the people who became known as the Yoruba, have been settled there for at least 5000 years.

Students of the Yoruba way of life have to accept that, despite their antiquity, the Yorubas relied mainly on their oral tradition and did not keep written records until relatively recently. Legends about Oduduwa abound in Yoruba history but are difficult to interpret. One account tells how God sent Obatala and Oduduwa to create the earth and the human race. Another claims that Oduduwa was a son of King Lammurudu of Mecca and that he came to West Africa from Arabia. In yet another, Oduduwa was an exiled prince who had been condemned to death over palace intrigues, but had been released by sympathetic executioners. He wandered about until he reached a place

74

he called "Ilefe" which meant "I have run to safety" and is obviously the origin of the name of Ile-Ife. This part of Africa was already inhabited when Oduduwa arrived and so the Yoruba language and much of the culture would have originated from those earlier residents. Whatever the truth, at the end of the first millennium Oduduwa set up the Ife state. Thirteen other such states, perhaps as many as 26, also appeared around Ile-Ife and became a loosely organised confederacy under Oduduwa's leadership.

The Yoruba system was highly decentralised with each state having its monarch. The various monarchs traced their origins and instruments of office to events in Ile-Ife and since Yoruba culture requires that citizenship is derived from being born into a family in a kingdom, all Yoruba people trace their origins back to Ile-Ife. Yorubas today in London, Lagos, Freetown and New York identify with Ile-Ife. Each state had its boundaries which were recognised by the others. States conducted relations bilaterally or multilaterally depending on circumstances, usually peacefully but sometimes in conflict. The Yoruba nation prospered with its economy firmly based on agriculture which flourished on the fertile land. Other Yoruba states emerged and competed with each other for power and influence. Within the Yoruba culture, the Oyo Empire became dominant for hundreds of years until the middle of the 19th century, but ever since AD 1000 Ile-Ife has held sway as the focus of Yoruba culture and tradition. Ile-Ife is to Yorubas what Mecca is to Muslims.

Around the middle of the 19th Century, after the abolition of slavery, Britain sought to develop trade with Yorubaland. The American Civil War disrupted cotton production and cotton supply to the Lancashire textile mills, so that for a while it became crucial for the British economy to procure alternative supplies. Experiments in cotton growing began in Yorubaland and for some years Britain obtained cotton from this source. By the end of the century Britain's need for cotton from West Africa had declined and cocoa, palm oil and rubber proved to be more valuable commodities. Missionaries were active in persuading the farmers in their congregations to grow these commercially valuable crops. Perhaps the Ministers of the local churches hoped that this economic activity would lead to increased giving during the part of the service when the offering was to be received!

Britain's efforts to develop trade with Yorubaland began in earnest in the 1840s and were initially concentrated on coastal regions and particularly on Lagos. Slaves remained the main export from Lagos with Portugal continuing to supply the market in Brazil long after Britain had abolished its part in the trade. The supremo of Lagos was a man called Kosoko and he refused to enter into any trading treaties with Britain in case his other sources of revenue were disturbed. This response was unpopular in Whitehall and in 1851 four British warships began bombarding Lagos forcing Kosoko to leave. Ten years later, Lagos became a British colony, so providing a bridgehead for the subsequent occupation of Yorubaland and the creation of Nigeria.

Who was Obafemi Awolowo and why did the authorities at the University of Ife decide to commemorate him by changing the institution's name in his honour in 1987? He was a most remarkable man who had a significant impact on the development of modern Nigeria. He was born on 6th March 1909 in Ikenne and he died there on the 7th May 1987. During his life he worked as a teacher, shorthand typist, journalist, businessman, trade unionist and politician. In his spare time worked for a degree in Commerce and in 1944 he came to the UK to study Law. On returning to Nigeria he founded the Action Group Party (AG) in 1951 and was elected Premier of the Western Region in 1954. He introduced free primary education in the Western Region in 1955.

Obafemi began to make his mark in national politics in 1960 when he became Leader of the Opposition in the Nigerian Federal Parliament. He was arrested, tried, found guilty of treason and sentenced to prison for ten years, but was released after three years in 1966. On two occasions he ran, unsuccessfully, for election as President of the Federal Republic. The value of his contributions to Nigerian life was recognized by his appointment as Grand Commander of the Federal Republic of Nigeria.

Obafemi Awolowo was an admired, or feared, Yoruba politician in the Federal Republic. He was an advocate of Yoruba ethnicity; how could he think otherwise as a Yoruba? Being one of the Yorubas is acquired through birth and cannot be renounced. The decentralised states of pre-colonial Yorubaland had functioned within a framework of national loyalty. The AG sought to work out the best deal for Yorubas in the newly independent Nigeria. The AG leaders saw federalism as the way forward for the new Nigeria, a return to a form of decentralisation such as had served the Yorubas so well for many centuries. Obafemi also realized, however, that national unity is necessary as the basis for a stable and fair society and in 1978 he inspired the establishment of the Unity Party. Obafemi

Awolowo's life could not have been better commemorated than by naming a university in his honour in Yorubaland.

* Extract from Voices from Twentieth Century Africa, by Chinweizu (1988). London and Boston: Faber and Faber.

Zebra

White men in Africa
Puffing at their pipes,
Think the zebra's a white horse
With black stripes.

Black men in Africa,
With pipes of different types,
Know the zebra's a black horse
With white stripes.

Gavin Ewart

Reproduced with permission from Margo Ewart from *The Learned Hippotamus* (1986). London: Hutchinson.

CHAPTER TEN

Medicines
Ancient and Modern

*"On 6 September 1906 Paul Ehrlich described the sub-
stances which would seek out and destroy the living
microbes in the body as magic bullets. The method
would be called chemotherapy."*

Reproduced from *Microbes and Men* by Robert Reid (1974). London:
British Broadcasting Corporation.

Deworming is a succinct, if ugly, word describing the
killing and expulsion of parasitic worms by means of
anthelminthic chemotherapy. In our society,
chemotherapy tends to be a term reserved for cancer
treatment, but chemotherapy has always been associated with the treatment of infectious agents by
means of specifically designed chemicals. Since parasitologists refer to worms as helminths, drug treatment to expel
them is known as anthelminthic chemotherapy. In developing countries local medicine men, herbalists and traditional
healers provide diverse forms of deworming. Take Mr
Onesmus Njoroge, the sometime proprietor of the Kenya
Country Herb Medicines Supply Company, whose practice
was based at the market place in Karatina between stalls
piled high with fruit and vegetables. He advertised that his

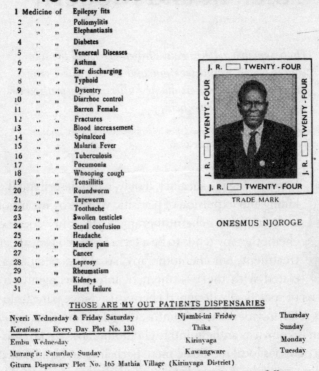

KENYA COUNTRY HERB MEDICINES SUPPLY Co.
P.O. BOX 324 NYERI & BOX 314 KARATINA
TEL. 230 KARATINA

ADVERTISEMENT OF VICTORY MEDICINES TO CURE THE FOLLOWING DISEASES

1 Medicine of	Epilepsy fits
2 ,, ,,	Poliomylitis
3 ,, ,,	Elephantiasis
4 ,, ,,	Diabetes
5 ,, ,,	Venereal Diseases
6 ,, ,,	Asthma
7 ,, ,,	Ear discharging
8 ,, ,,	Typhoid
9 ,, ,,	Dysentry
10 ,, ,,	Diarrhoe control
11 ,, ,,	Barren Female
12 ,, ,,	Fractures
13 ,, ,,	Blood increasement
14 ,, ,,	Spinalcord
15 ,, ,,	Malaria Fever
16 ,, ,,	Tuberculosis
17 ,, ,,	Pneumonia
18 ,, ,,	Whooping cough
19 ,, ,,	Tonsillitis
20 ,, ,,	Roundworm
21 ,, ,,	Tapeworm
22 ,, ,,	Toothache
23 ,, ,,	Swollen testicles
24 ,, ,,	Senal confusion
25 ,, ,,	Headache
26 ,, ,,	Muscle pain
27 ,, ,,	Cancer
28 ,, ,,	Leprosy
29 ,, ,,	Rheumatism
30 ,, ,,	Kidneys
31 ,, ,,	Heart failure

J. R. ☐ TWENTY - FOUR

J. R. ☐ TWENTY - FOUR

TRADE MARK

ONESMUS NJOROGE

THOSE ARE MY OUT PATIENTS DISPENSARIES

Nyeri:	Wednesday & Friday Saturday	Njambi-ini	Friday	Thursday
Karatina:	Every Day Plot No. 130	Thika		Sunday
Embu	Wednesday	Kirinyaga		Monday
Murang'a:	Saturday Sunday	Kawangware		Tuesday

Gituru Dispensary Plot No. 165 Mathia Village (Kirinyaga District)

I have cured the above diseases sincerely & successfully.
I am 52 years experienced with this invention of medicines.

PRINTED BY NYERI PRINTING PRESS P.O. Box 441 Phone 2049 NYERI.

Advertising a panacea for all our ills.

herbal prescriptions could cure numerous ailments including worm infections, heart failure, cancer, malaria and tuberculosis. Mr Njoroge and those like him sincerely believe that they can heal the sick and their patients believe it too. For centuries, European medicine was based largely on herbs. Any city in Britain boasting a Botanic Garden is likely to host an ancient University with a long established Medical School.

It started me thinking .... about how our use of medicines might have begun. Did our ancestors learn from watching animals, assuming that animals actually do take medicine? More importantly, in view of the costs faced by the research-based pharmaceutical industry, can we realistically expect the appearance of new deworming drugs given the spending power of people who live where worm-induced disease holds sway? Should we not be drawing attention to the merits of local herbal preparations in the war against worms?

In 1892 Sir William Ostler published *Principles and Practice of Medicine* and the western medical profession has been blessed by the foundation he laid. Sir William is attributed as having remarked that the desire to take medicine is perhaps the greatest feature which distinguishes man from animals. Recent observations, however, show that chimpanzees, our nearest relatives, may treat themselves with medicinal plants, a behavioural pattern that can be interpreted as an anti-parasite activity. Chimps deworm themselves by using plants in such a way that they avoid the harmful part of the plant and ingest the beneficial part. Apparently, young chimps acquire the habit by watching sick adults treating themselves.

In Tanzania, chimpanzees have been seen to select the rough-surfaced leaves of plants of the genus *Aspilia*, fold them and swallow them whole. Examination of chimp stools reveals that the leaves pass through undigested but still folded and that intestinal worms become trapped in the folds. The leaves act like mobile forceps plucking worms off the surface of the gut and carrying them out of the host. Michael Huffman and colleagues, who studied the use of plants for medicinal purposes by chimpanzees, refer to this as the "Velcro effect". Chimpanzees also remove and chew the bitter pith of plants of the genus *Vernonia*, presumably to rid themselves of intestinal infections. Bears, porcupines and birds select plants, apparently to promote and maintain their health. Evidence about when humans began to use plants as medicine is hard to find, but there is a legend amongst the Navajo people that kodiak bears taught them to rely on the therapeutic powers of roots of *Ligusticum porteri* for the treatment of intestinal infections.

Worm infections must have been relatively common in Lancashire even as late as the 1930s. My mother trained as a nurse at Bolton Royal Infirmary which closed in 1996 after 114 years of caring for local people. In her copy of the fourth edition of *Text-Book for Nurses* by E.W. Hey Groves and J.M. Fortescue-Brickdale published by Oxford University Press in 1930 there is a section covering diseases caused by intestinal worms. Some of the prescriptions for treatment must have been most unpleasant and dangerous – certainly not chemotherapy as defined by Paul

Ehrlich. Depending on diagnosis, patients had to endure oral doses of substances such as santonin, turpentine, benzine, thymol, oil of chenopodium, carbon tetrachloride and chloroform, plus purging to keep "the bowels well open". My mother told me that as a junior nurse, she had to search through the stools of patients treated for tapeworm to find the "head". The so-called head is the scolex by which the tapeworm attaches itself to the intestinal wall. The tissue immediately behind the scolex has remarkable powers of regeneration giving the animal the potential to produce a new body. The late Clark P. Read kept the same tapeworm alive for 14 years by routine surgical transplantation of its anterior end from rat to rat. The experiment ended when the recipient rat died while Read was unavailable to carry out the transplant.

There is no doubt that we need a non-stop supply of safe, effective, easily administered and affordable drugs for the treatment of worm infections of all kinds in humans and livestock. Affordability is the overriding concern. In industrialised countries the need now is for the expulsion of worms from domestic and companion animals, so drug costs can be recovered by the pharmaceutical industry through the pricing structure. That situation does not exist in many developing countries. Wealth is hugely skewed so that only a few people can afford private medical care and expensive drugs. The Ministries of Health in developing countries cannot meet the costs of national drug bills. For example in 1990 in Japan, USD 412 *per capita* was available for health care, whereas in Bangladesh the figure at the same time was USD 2 *per capita*. A first-class deworming programme can be run at a cost as low as a few US cents *per capita* per year, but governments cannot afford to spend so much of the annual health budget on deworming. Currently, deworming programmes depend on the generosity of western pharmaceutical companies and donor agencies outwith the countries where worm disease is endemic. What would happen to deworming if these sources of resource stopped or diminished?

At first sight, we might be inclined to criticise the research-based pharmaceutical companies over the costs of drugs. Costs are inevitably high, however, because of the standards set in the western world for achieving drug quality and safety testing. During the past 20 years or so, one major European pharmaceutical company invested over £3 billion in research and development leading to the synthesis of some 200,000 new compounds. Of these, 110 advanced into the development process and eventually 12 new products were launched. Those statistics explain why drugs originating in the research-based pharmaceutical industry are expensive. In the case of drugs needed to treat worm-induced diseases, the managers of pharmaceutical companies have to decide whether the costs of producing a new drug could ever be recovered from the countries where the need exists; shareholders have to be content in terms of both financial rewards and company policies.

New drugs for deworming could be needed to overcome the threat of drug resistance. Resistance to many potent antibiotics has developed in pathogenic bacteria. The emergence of antibiotic resistance is considered by some authorities to be an even greater threat to public health than the emergence of a new disease. Is it only a matter of time before populations of human intestinal worms become resistant to the commonly used deworming drugs? In this context, resistance is the inherited ability of a worm to survive the concentration of drug normally prescribed to kill or immobilise it before expulsion from the host.

The development of resistance will depend on how worms respond to the use of a drug, perhaps of dubious quality, in an infected community. Imagine a population of worms established in people living on an island into which no new worms arrive from outside the island. The existing population of worms will maintain itself through natural interbreeding. The arrival of a public health programme designed to control worm-induced disease will bring an anthelminthic drug to the island's residents. Theory indicates that resistance will emerge as a consequence of how the genes (DNA) of individual worms respond to the selection pressure caused by how the drug is used. Drug pressure results from the frequency of dosing, the quality of the ingredients in the drug, and the dose given. In our theoretical, isolated population of worms, the appearance of resistance might occur after a few or several generations; the shorter the worm's generation time, the more rapid the development of resistance. Of course, people are rarely so isolated and any who migrate, travel on business or visit relatives may take worms with them thereby bringing new worm DNA into the community. The new DNA will tend to relieve or delay the selection pressure imposed by drug use because the new worms will interbreed with the existing ones.

Some species of nematode worm now express inherited resistance to deworming drugs, but so far reports about resistance in the worms commonly found in humans are rare and in need of rigorous confirmation. Worms causing a serious wasting disease in sheep are resistant to some of our most reliable families of drugs. The resistance is passed on to the progeny and the actual genes have been identified. When these genes are selected and expressed, the drugs are unable to affect their target cells in the worm.

Even if we have a strong case for pressing pharmaceutical companies to develop new types of drug to which worms have never previously been exposed, the costs will not be recovered because the needy cannot afford them; there is no realistic market unless aid agencies continue to foot the bill. Alternative affordable approaches are required for reducing the burden of human disease caused by worm infections. Herbal deworming recipes used in so many communities often have great efficacy. Herbal prescriptions have important properties; transport costs are minimal, importation paperwork is not needed, traditional practitioners and the raw materials are on the spot and local people trust them.

Evidence for the benefits of herbal medicine for the treatment of worm infections came from working with colleagues in China. For thousands of years, the practitioners of Traditional Chinese Medicine (TCM) have recorded their prescriptions for the treatment of all kinds of ailments and infections. The methods of TCM diagnosis and interpretation of the patient's signs and symptoms require years of training. The body of prescribing knowledge in TCM is immense, nearly 62,000 prescriptions having been recorded. About 7,000 species of medicinal plants grow in China and their use has stood the test of time. Modern TCM strongly advocates the use of prescriptions based solely on plant products; practitioners are directed to avoid the parts and organs of animals, regardless of whether they are endangered or not, in the medicines they prepare.

One example shows how a TCM prescription can be effective for the treatment of roundworm disease when administered by trained practitioners. From time to time individual *Ascaris lumbricoides* move out of the small intestine and crawl up the common bile duct towards the liver. Such wandering worms block the bile duct, reach the gallbladder, enter the liver or penetrate the pancreas. Biliary ascariasis, as this condition is called, is unpleasant and life-threatening. Patients relying on western medicine are likely to be advised to have a general anaesthetic and undergo abdominal surgery to extract the worms. Surgery may not be an option for many people enduring biliary ascariasis, and TCM has a prescription for its treatment. Traditional doctors prepare *decoction of fructus mume* for their patients from a mixture based on nine plants. In a survey of publications about the use of this type of prescription for the treatment of biliary ascariasis in China, colleagues found that out of 4167 cases, full cure was achieved in 4060 cases, significant improvement occurred in a further 77, while only a few eventually needed surgery.

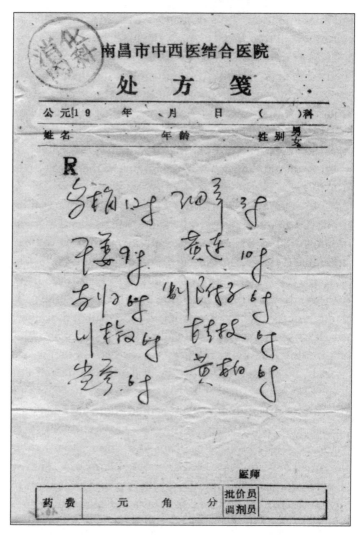

Chinese prescription for the decoction of fructus mume *for the treatment of biliary ascariasis.*

Complementary medicine seems to have blossomed and outlets for treatments prepared by traditional methods are to be found in many British towns and cities. My background as a natural scientist still constrains me to rely on medicines developed, tested and regulated by western processes. I think we need to know about the pharmacology, pharmacokinetics and mode of action of herbal treatments such as *decoction of fructus mume*. Nevertheless, if communities have remedies on the doorstep that can bring some measure of relief to poor people from the plague of worm infections we should not discourage use unless something better is to hand. Local knowledge is crucial for the harvesting of the correct plants, the preparation of the prescriptions and their safe use.

> *"Traditional medicine has made a great contribution to the welfare of all nations in the world. ..... Traditional Chinese medicine, with its rich clinical experience, its unique theoretical system and its extensive literature has served to combat illness among the Chinese people for many centuries. .....We firmly believe that the integration of traditional medicine with modern medicine helps to correct the deficiencies of each and will certainly promote the development of medical science in the future."*

Reproduced with permission from the World Health Organization from *Traditional Chinese Medicine* by Wang Pei (1983) pp 68 – 75 in *Traditional Medicine and Health Care Coverage* (eds R.H. Bannerman, J. Burton and Ch'en Wen-Chieh). Geneva: World Health Organization.

CHAPTER ELEVEN

Off the Road to Mandalay

"Chindits never die — they go to heaven and regroup. They have already been to hell."

www.chindit.org.uk (2006)

During the 1980s, researchers in my field were embroiled in a lively debate. Did infection of children with the common roundworm, living in the small intestine and so occupying a prime site for disturbing appetite, digestion and nutrition, have adverse effects on the growth and development of those children? There is now consensus that worm infections weaken children, particularly in countries where the quality and quantity of daily food is not always adequate. One relevant study was carried out in Burma, later to become Myanmar, by colleagues from the government's Department of Medical Research in Rangoon, which became Yangon at the same time. I worked in Burma to help plan the study and later monitor its progress. The findings showed quite conclusively that when children were kept worm free by having a few doses of deworming medicine each year, they gained more weight and grew taller than

91

similar children who were not dewormed. No extra food was offered; regular deworming was the only intervention.

On 10th December 1982 we were driving along the road to Mandalay. Some miles out of Rangoon, was a sign to Taukkyan Military Cemetery. When I asked to see the place my friends obligingly turned off the road and took me to the cemetery. I don't know why I had such an urgent need to visit this sanctuary. It was carefully tended and had rows of graves each with a grey headstone. I stood before one and photographed it; in relief was a familiar cap badge and beneath was the inscription, "4199477 Private T. H. GRIFFITHS, The King's Own Royal Regt. 14th May 1944. Age 28". There were the graves of other soldiers from the King's Own. The cap badge was familiar because I had worn it twelve years after the death of Private Griffiths. I was much moved at the time; my friends from Rangoon thought I had found the last resting place of a dear relative.

It started me thinking .... at first about the regiment and then about its soldiers who had served and died in Burma. The regiment was raised in the West Country by

Cap badge of the King's Own Royal Regiment (Lancaster).

the Earl of Plymouth in 1680 for service in Tangiers. On returning to England it became a unit in the permanent army and was designated the 4th of Foot. In 1715, the 4th also became the King's Own Regiment by royal warrant of King

George I and, after the government's re-organisation of the army in 1881, it moved to a permanent depot in Lancaster and became the King's Own Royal Regiment (Lancaster). I wondered how much of that Private Griffiths had learnt during basic training at Bowerham Barracks.

So what was Private Griffiths doing in Burma during World War II and how did he and his comrades die so far away from the regiment's traditional recruiting area of North Lancashire and Westmorland? Perhaps he had been one of Orde Wingate's Chindits and perhaps he might have died from malaria. In May, 1942, Major-General Orde Wingate assembled and trained a mixed fighting force of British, Gurkha, Indian and Burmese soldiers to penetrate deep behind Japanese lines with the purpose of destroying bridges, blowing up fuel dumps, ambushing convoys and cutting communications. Wingate called this force the Chindits after a mythical beast known as the Chinthe which guards the temples and monasteries of Burma. The Chindits carried out two major expeditions of sabotage and much hand-to-hand fighting. Wingate's military plans did not achieve all he hoped for because of problems over maintaining supplies behind enemy lines. But the Chindits proved that Japanese soldiers were not the only ones who could fight in the jungle.

Soldiers of the 2nd Battalion King's Own Royal Regiment served in the second Chindit expedition from November 1943 to June 1944. The activities of the Chindits would have occupied a considerable part of the Japanese army in Burma and so aided the steady advance of General "Vinegar" Joe Stilwell's troops and the eventual liberation of the country. General Wingate died in an air crash on 24 March 1944, a few weeks before Private Griffiths. I like to think they might have met, since Wingate made various visits to the King's Own when the second expedition of Chindits was being organised. The soldiers of the King's Own cut and fought their way through 1,100 miles of Burmese jungle during this time. For this period of sustained bravery and endurance the regiment was awarded the battle honour 'Chindits 1944' which is emblazoned on the colours laid up in the Regimental Chapel in Lancaster Priory Church. I like to think that Private Griffiths helped to earn that honour for the regiment.

In an attempt to confirm my notion that Pte Griffiths had been a Chindit, I consulted the Commonwealth War Graves Commission. Taukkyan Cemetery was established in 1951 for the reception of graves from battlefield cemeteries at Akyab, Mandalay, Meiktila and Sahmaw. The cemetery at Sahmaw was an original Chindit cemetery for soldiers who had died in the battle for Myitkyina. Importantly, I also learnt that Pte Griffiths served in the regiment's 2nd battalion which fought at Myitkyina during May 1944. He could well have been a Chindit who died in that battle.

For all that being a Chindit was dangerous, Private Griffiths must have been at risk from bouts of malaria. In her history of the King's Own, Julia Cowper wrote "All Chindits were by now completely exhausted, emaciated and rotten with malaria"*. Despite all the best efforts of modern medical science malaria remains one of the nastiest and deadliest infectious diseases. Malaria occurs in one

94

hundred or so countries today, threatening a third of the world's population. About five hundred million suffer from malaria and from 1.5 to 2.5 million people die every year from the disease. Most of the deaths are of infants in sub-Saharan Africa.

Malaria parasites are transmitted by female mosquitoes which inject microscopic organisms as they take a blood meal from a susceptible victim. Some seventy species of mosquito are able to transmit malaria parasites. The insects are not simply vectors; they are necessary for the parasite to complete its development. After the mosquito has bitten, the tiny parasites pass through the blood stream to the liver, where they enter liver cells and multiply. Next they burst out of the liver cells and invade red blood cells, multiplying and bursting forth with the destruction of many precious cells. This activity, culminating in the destruction of blood cells, is accompanied by bouts of high fever and continues until the infection subsides or the patient dies. It is no wonder that chronic disease occurs and that death often results, especially in people who have had little exposure to malaria parasites and so have no immunity. This lack of immunity explains why so many African babies die from malaria. Similarly, Private Griffiths and his fellow soldiers from Lancashire would have had little opportunity to develop immunity.

Military historians have noted how malaria has often influenced the course of a campaign. During World War II in the Far Eastern theatre, tactics were in large measure determined by the presence of malaria.

Malaria had particularly devastating effects in Burma. During 1943 the hospital admission rate for European troops suffering from malaria alone was 628 cases per 1000 men. This meant that malaria claimed 45 times as many victims as did battles in that war-torn country.

The progress of the Japanese invasion in the early years of World War II cut off the allies' supply of quinine for malaria treatment. Depriving the allies of quinine was a form of passive biological warfare. The situation prompted a huge effort in the USA and UK to synthesise prophylactic and curative drugs. Insecticides were developed to kill mosquitoes and troops were issued with mosquito nets and insect repellent creams. Britain gave the production of DDT high wartime priority along with radar and penicillin. Mepacrine was one of the new drugs that could have been issued to Private Griffiths and his comrades. The drug was taken daily in tablet form, but it had unpleasant side effects including a bitter taste, the tendency to induce nausea and the likelihood of causing skin to turn yellow. Unfortunately, a rumour circulated that mepacrine caused impotency, so gullible soldiers refused their antimalarial drugs and risked malaria instead. The situation became so serious that commanding officers faced disciplinary action if the malaria-case rate among their men did not fall after the protective measures had been introduced.

Malaria statistics from World War II draw attention to the concern that societies have about the use of biological agents as offensive weapons. Long before scientific knowledge of pathogens or toxins existed, military men sought to infect or poison their opponents. Fomites, objects such as putrefying corpses, were flung into the defences of the besieged. The German government had a sophisticated programme of germ and chemical technology during World War I. In response to this and particularly as a result of the deployment of poisonous gases during that conflict, the first diplomatic attempt to limit unconventional warfare was held in Geneva in 1925. The outcome was the Geneva Protocol for the Prohibition of the Use in War of Asphyxiating, Poisonous or Other Gases, and of Bacteriological Methods of Warfare. The treaty prohibited *use*; there is still no satisfactory way of monitoring whether research and development are in progress.

Some shocking episodes concerning biological weapons have occurred during recent human history, none more so than the experiments carried out by the Japanese military in occupied Manchuria from 1932 until the end of World War II. This infamous programme was managed by Unit 731 and contained 150 buildings, 5 satellite camps and a staff of over 3000 scientists and technicians. In order to test the virulence and potency of various pathogens, prisoners were infected with organisms responsible for anthrax, cholera, meningitis and plague. Some 10,000 of them died either directly from disease or from execution to enable the staff to examine the progress of the infection. Staff of Unit 731, when captured and charged with war crimes, later admitted to Soviet prosecutors that at least 11 Chinese cities had been attacked with biological agents. Fifteen million fleas carrying the plague germ were dropped into one city and in another 10,000 cases of cholera were deliberately induced.

From 1943 until 1969, the United States carried out an offensive biological research programme at Fort Derrick, Maryland. The programme concentrated on plant pathogens designed to cause crop failure as well as pathogens known to cause disease in humans. US records have been open to scrutiny and during this period of intensive experimentation with pathogens, the rate of occupational infection was within nationally accepted standards. Implicit here should be confidence that the US scientists developed best safety practice for dealing with the consequences of biological attack. Somewhat surprisingly, 50 years passed before the US government decided to ratify the Geneva Protocol although its stockpiles of various lethal, incapacitating and anti-crop agents had been destroyed.

The devastating effects of malaria during the Burma campaign and the activities of Unit 731 show why governments fear biological weapons. The measures introduced then to counter malaria show how times of war can accelerate research and development for dealing with disease. Despite the knowledge of malaria gained in Burma and elsewhere, some 1.5 billion people live without protection from the disease. Mosquitoes were not expected to acquire resistance to insecticides or malaria parasites to develop resistance to curative drugs. Meanwhile let us not forget Private Griffiths, one of the 859 men of the King's Own who died during World War II. At least that is a better statistic than the total of 6515 men of the reg-

iment killed by bullets and disease in Flanders during
World War I.

*Extract reproduced from The King's Own, Vol. III by J.M. Cowper (1957). Alder-
shot: Gale & Polden Ltd.

> *"I know this little thing*
> *A myriad men will save.*
> *O Death, where is thy sting?*
> *Thy victory, O Grave?"*

Verse sent by Ronald Ross in a letter to his wife after he found malaria
parasites in female anophiline mosquitoes on 20th August 1897. Reproduced from *Ronald Ross* by R.L. Megroz (1931). London: George
Allen & Unwin Ltd.

CHAPTER TWELVE

Advice from Uncle Azael

*"I like trees because they seem more resigned to the way
they have to live than other things do."*

Reproduced with permission from *O Pioneers!* by Willa Cather (1913).
London: Virago Press, an imprint of Little, Brown Book Group.

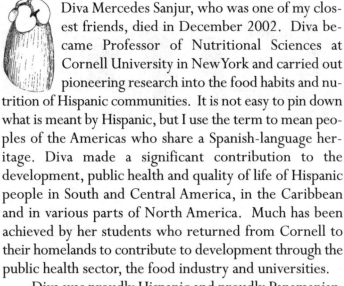Diva Mercedes Sanjur, who was one of my clos-
est friends, died in December 2002. Diva be-
came Professor of Nutritional Sciences at
Cornell University in New York and carried out
pioneering research into the food habits and nutrition of Hispanic communities. It is not easy to pin down
what is meant by Hispanic, but I use the term to mean peo-
ples of the Americas who share a Spanish-language heritage. Diva made a significant contribution to the
development, public health and quality of life of Hispanic
people in South and Central America, in the Caribbean
and in various parts of North America. Much has been
achieved by her students who returned from Cornell to
their homelands to contribute to development through the
public health sector, the food industry and universities.

Diva was proudly Hispanic and proudly Panamanian.
One day when working in Panama with her on a survey of
the nutritional status of the Guaymi Indians in Chiriqui
Province, she took me to her home town of Remedios in

Church of Nuestra Senora de los Remedios, *Chiriqui province, Panama.*

the eastern part of Chiriqui. Remedios is a sleepy place with a splendid 17th century Spanish-style church at its centre. A short walk, albeit in a hot and humid atmosphere, takes you to the coast, where gentle Pacific breakers roll up and down the golden beach and sand crabs scuttle in and out of their burrows. Further along the coast, in 1513, Vasco Nunez de Balboa was the first recorded European to look out across this peaceful sea which he claimed for Spain and called the Pacific Ocean.

Before we left Remedios Diva took me to meet her

Uncle Azael and her Aunt Maria, who welcomed and re-freshed us before we returned to the Guaymi project. Uncle Azael had long been retired as Head Teacher of the school in Remedios. He had taught Diva and was ex-tremely proud of his niece and star pupil. Kofi Annan, while Secretary-General of the United Nations, wrote that study after study has taught us that there is no tool for de-velopment more effective than the education of girls.* Diva and Uncle Azael were proof of that.

When Diva left school and Remedios, Uncle Azael gave her three pieces of advice; learn English, learn to type and plant a tree. To learn English seemed sound with the USA such a dominant influence in the region and to learn to type was also sound at the time because a smart young woman would at least get a job in an office and so be able to pay the bills. Today we might convert his advice to learn English to learn another language and rather than learn to type, to become computer literate. But what about the ad-vice to plant a tree?

It started me thinking .... about trees. When I was a boy the trees, rhododendrons and privet hedges in Bolton had trunks, twigs and leaves coated with soot and grime from the chimneys of mills, houses and railway engines. Grime was everywhere, on pavements, buildings and fences. We inhaled grime with every intake of breath. On a clear day, we could walk along the Scout Road, well above the north of the town, and look over the Lancashire plain with its mill chimneys, pit winding gears and slag heaps. Usually, however, definition was impaired because there would be a low pall of grey smoke. The pollution deposited on the tree trunks provided biologists with an opportunity to study natural selection and offered tangible evidence for Darwin's theory of evolution. Two forms of the Peppered Moth were known to occur in England, a light-coloured form and a dark form. The light form is hard to spot on trees with clean trunks while the dark form is equally well camouflaged on trees with sooty trunks. Light forms on sooty trunks and dark forms on clean trunks are easy prey for predatory birds. Dark moths were first observed in England in 1848, but by the 1950s in industrial areas 99% of Peppered Moths were of the dark form.

I wonder if anyone had studied the impact of this dirt on the photosynthetic activity of the trees and their role in absorbing carbon dioxide and releasing oxygen. I also wondered if Uncle Azael was already anxious about the destruction of tropical rain forests. Tropical rain forests or, as some experts prefer to call them tropical moist forests, are forests that are evergreen, hygrophilous or water-loving in character, with some plants at least thirty metres high, rich in thick-stemmed lianas and supporting woody as well as herbaceous epiphytes. Climatic conditions are central to the definition and classification of tropical rain forests; in all cases the mean temperature should be at least $18°C$ and the annual rainfall should be at least 1700mm. If we had possessed satellite technology one hundred and fifty years ago, we would have detected a green band lying across all the land between ten degrees north and ten degrees south of the equator. That is not the case today. Of our original 15.5 million square kilometres of tropical rain forest, estimates suggest that only 9 million remain; we are losing it at a rate of some 168,000 square kilometres per year. These forests are the homes to many people, providing them with shelter, food, clothing, fuel, medicines, building materials and other resources. Now the forests serve as the origins of these resources for millions more people living elsewhere. As the forests decline, so does the habitat for at least half of all known species of free-living plants and animals. Ecologists have calculated that roughly 27000 species, mainly insects and plants, disappear annually from our dwindling rain forests. As the forests decline so do natural regulators of water flow, climate modulation and soil erosion. Somehow we have to stop destroying the earth's tropical rain forests. Was that what Uncle Azael had in mind when he told his niece to plant a tree? Two thirds of the forests of India, Myanmar and Sri Lanka have already gone. Best estimates suggest that for every ten units of forest destroyed only the trees of one are replaced.

Human activity is solely responsible for the rate of decimation of tropical rain forests. Trees are cleared for commercial crops such as rubber, coffee, tea, sugar, tobacco and palm oil. Trees are cleared for pulpwood for paper and hardwood for buildings and furniture. Panama's trees produce first class cocobolo wood, rosewood, mahogany, purpleheart and lignum vitae among others. Logging, whether for timber in its own right, or to clear the way for mining, oil drilling, hydroelectric schemes and road construction, is extraordinarily quick and simple given the power of modern chain saws, tractors and other machinery. Trees are cleared for cattle ranching to satisfy the worldwide demand for hamburgers. Unfortunately, tropical rain forests are not replaced simply by planting trees. Uncle Azael's advice may be excellent and has immense educational value. If a tree were planted today by or for every member of the world's population then six billion more trees would probably improve the situation. However, wholesale logging in tropical rain forests damages an ecosystem of which the trees form a part. We can destroy the forests but we cannot replace them.

Some developing countries have tried to reconcile the conflict between the need of local people to earn a living from the forests and the problems caused by the resulting deforestation. Plan Sierra in the Dominican Republic was established by the government to prevent and reverse significant deforestation while improving the economic opportunities of local people. The scheme was managed from Santiago near the tree-clad mountains in the northwest of the country. Much of the country's rainfall occurs there and the fast flowing rivers offer an effective source of hydro-electric power. Dams and power stations had been built and the government had looked forward to providing the country's industries and services with cheap power and taking deserved credit for the provision.

Deforestation, however, was making the steep mountainsides unstable and the heavy rains brought about widespread erosion, with soil washing into the rivers, blocking the water flow and disrupting the power supply. Plan Sierra worked to reduce deforestation by offering people other sources of income such as fish farming, pig rearing and furniture making, linked in turn to replanting and managing the forests as dynamic, living resources. As

Rocking chair from Santiago, Dominican Republic.

such, the communities prospered and so did their health care and educational provision.

There is one aspect of forest destruction which is difficult to condemn. Many people have no option but to fell trees for fuel. About 80% of households in developing countries depend entirely on wood as their primary source of energy. Such is the demand for firewood that there is every prospect of its being exhausted even before the oil wells have been pumped dry. How are poor people supposed to cook their food or boil their water if they are denied firewood? There is no gas to turn on or electricity to use, although some ingenious folk in Asia manage to light their homes and cook by burning gas released from decomposing pig and buffalo dung. Others burn dried dung as a source of energy instead of using it as a fertilizer for their crops.

Firewood is rarely available for the populations of the slums of developing countries. Charcoal has become a main source of domestic fuel and at a cost to the forests. About 4 small trees must be felled to produce 30 kg of charcoal. Charcoal is not as efficient a fuel as we may think. It may be clean and easy to use but some of the energy from its starting wood is lost during preparation.

107

Some developing countries are exporting charcoal as a foreign currency earner, again to the detriment of their precious forests. I wonder if we in the industrialised countries understand or ever think about the huge deficit that now exists for domestic fuel in so many places. What a sorry state we have reached; many of our fellows are already paying more for the fuel to cook a meal than for the food itself.

*Extract from *The State of the World's Children 2004*. New York: United Nations Children's Fund (UNICEF).

"Trees are of course at the heart of things. How could it be otherwise? The human lineage began in trees. We have left our first ancestors far behind but we are creatures of the forest still."

Reproduced with permission from *The Secret Lives of Trees* by Colin Tudge (2005). (© Colin Tudge). London: Penguin Books/New York: Random House Inc.

CHAPTER THIRTEEN

From Richford to Riches

"The duodenum, the whole jejunum and even the upper half of the ileum were completely filled with fresh, red, partly coagulated blood. Thousands of ancylostomes were hanging in the mucosa of the small intestine, each with its own small petechia resembling the bite of a leech."

Reproduced with permission from CAB International the "Extract" from Wilhelm Griesinger (1854) quoted by David Grove in *A History of Human Helminthology* (1990). Wallingford, Oxon.: CAB International.

 Cornell University dominates the city of Ithaca in the Finger Lakes region of New York State. Ithaca is some 250 miles by road from JFK airport. I think the most scenic drive is to follow route 17 through the Catskill Mountains, take refreshment at Roscoe Diner, skirt around Binghamton, near the Pennsylvania state line, and then drive north along Interstate 81 as far as Whitney Point. A short drive westwards along route 79 brings you to Ithaca. This section of route 79 winds and undulates through deeply forested country. The forest is described as secondary forest because the present trees, dominated by maples, colonised the farmland left by the families who, once President Lincoln signed the Homestead Act into law in

1862, went west to look for more and better land. Every few miles through this densely wooded terrain, the road reaches small, seemingly unkempt townships in which you can suspect poverty. The mainly wooden-clad houses seem to need a paint job, or treatment for rot, or have their screens replaced or have rusting pickup trucks removed from their yards.

One of these communities is called Richford. There is little on show, other than a weathered wooden board telling passing travellers that on 8th July 1839 a baby boy was born to Elizabeth (née Davison) and William Avery Rockefeller. The happy parents, devout Baptists, named their son John Davison. In due course, John D. Rockefeller became the world's most feared, successful and wealthy businessman - and the world's most generous philanthropist. Rockefeller became concerned with the effect of hookworm infections on human health and his generosity did much to advance knowledge of the problem and how to resolve it. It started me thinking .... about the circumstances which drove John D. Rockefeller to direct wealth to deal with hookworms.

The World Health Organization estimates that about 900 million people are infected with hookworms. There are two main species, *Necator amer-*

Roadside notice in Richford, New York, commemorating the life of John Davison Rockefeller in 1839.

110

icanus and *Ancylostoma duodenale*; the former is more common than the latter. *Necator* prevails throughout developing countries in the tropics and sub-tropics, while *Ancylostoma* tends to predominate in colder climates where subtropical countries merge with those in temperate zones. *Ancylostoma* was first recognized in mainland Europe during the 19th century. A year before Rockefeller's birth an Italian physician called Angelo Dubini published the first detailed description of hookworms after carrying out an autopsy on a woman who died in Milan. Later he attributed the deaths of other patients to hookworms, but little attention was paid to his concerns until the construction of the St Gotthard railway tunnel, connecting northern Italy and southern Switzerland, was halted when many of the labourers collapsed with severe anaemia. In this case, as in millions of cases worldwide today, the anaemia was caused by the feeding activity of hookworms in the gut. Hookworms are the vampires of the human gut. They bite into the gut wall and suck blood from tiny veins and capillaries. Like so many blood feeders, they produce an anticoagulant to stop the blood from clotting. When they stop feeding and release their grip on the gut wall, bleeding continues and the host's vitality is further sapped.

Anaemic people cannot carry out sustained heavy work such as that needed to grow food, irrigate crops and develop their countries. Anaemic women often have difficult pregnancies and produce babies of low birth weight. Anaemic children develop slowly and have impaired cognitive performance. Even if detectable anaemia does not occur, the presence of the hookworms can induce persist-

111

ent iron deficiency. Hookworm disease is defined today as iron deficiency associated with hookworm infection. As with all worm infections, the development and severity of disease depend on the general health of the host and the number of worms present. A woman passing more than 5000 hookworm eggs per gram of faeces will be losing about 10 ml of blood per day. While many hookworms might be needed to cause anaemia in a Nebraskan farmer with access to all that iron-rich beef; even a few hookworms would damage a poor Indian farmer with little access to meat of any kind.

The life history of hookworms is straightforward. Adult worms mate in the human gut and the females release fertile eggs which pass out in the stools, contaminating the environment. Hookworms thrive where sanitation is lacking or inadequate. A tiny juvenile worm emerges from each egg, feeds, grows and moults to produce another juvenile stage which then moults again. The resulting juvenile stops feeding and climbs to the tips of blades of grass and twigs and, if bare human skin brushes past, the young worm grabs hold, penetrates the skin and so gains entry to its host. Once inside the body, the hookworm makes its way, growing and moulting en route, back to the gut. The adult worms measure from 10 to 15mm and they live for one to two years. Wearing shoes would greatly reduce the prevalence of hookworm infection, but poor people cannot afford shoes. In some places, attendance at school requires the pupils to wear shoes. So the children carry their precious shoes to and from school to make them last longer and wear them in the classroom only.

112

At the beginning of the 20th century the government of Great Britain became anxious about the possible establishment and economic impact of hookworm infection in the country's coal mines. At the time, hookworm infection affected coal miners in Westphalia; the warm, moist conditions in the coal mines favoured the development and survival of the infective juveniles. What would happen if any infected miners came to work in Britain? The government commissioned J.S. Haldane for advice about how to deal with the threat. Not surprisingly he recommended the provision of basic sanitation (buckets) for the miners thereby preventing

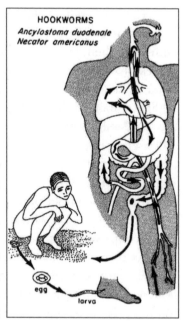

Life cycle of hookworms (Ancylostoma duodenale *and* Necator americanus) *drawn by Paula DiSanto Bensadoun from* Parasites and People *by D. W. T. C. and published by Macmillan.* Ancylostoma *was the common hookworm in Europe and* Necator *in the southern states of the USA.*

contamination of the environment. If an infected miner had had to relieve himself underground at the coal face, conditions could have favoured a hookworm epidemic. In any event the problem never arose in the coal mines, but Cornish tin miners were affected for a time.

113

The Rockefellers of Richford were soon on the move. They went to Moravia, NY, in 1843, to Owego, NY, in 1850 and then to Strongville, Ohio, in 1853. Further moves took place in Ohio with the family finally settling in Cleveland. John, aged 16, began his business career on 26 September 1855 as a junior clerk and book-keeper in the wholesale firm of Hewitt and Tuttle. He resigned in 1859 when his request for a pay rise was declined, borrowed USD 1,000 from his father, at a rate of interest of 10%, and joined forces with Maurice B. Clark. They had seen the commercial opportunities that might emerge from a Civil War. The Union won the war largely because their troops were supported by heavy industry. Rockefeller, in turn, noted that industry depended on energy and he and Clark teamed up with Samuel Andrews who was skilled in refining crude oil. The rest is history. John Davison Rockefeller brushed aside or engulfed all competition, monopolising the US energy sector with his Standard Oil Company until legislation was passed in Congress to break his industrial stranglehold. Rockefeller's personal fortune reached, in today's terms, USD 125 billion.

For much of his lifetime - and he lived until 23 May 1937 - Rockefeller seems to have been vilified in the US press as a dangerously powerful menace to society. It was implied that his philanthropy was some form of penance, an attempt to salve his troubled conscience over all his ruthless business deals. That is far from the truth. Throughout his long life Rockefeller was totally committed to the practice of giving. When he began work for Hewitt and Tuttle he opened his now famous Ledger A in

114

which all his personal financial affairs were recorded. Despite earning as little as USD 6 per month, he supported the Baptist Church, missionary work, Catholic orphans and schools for black Americans. As his wealth grew, so did his giving, but a defined philanthropic strategy did not emerge until 1892 when he joined forces with Frederick Gates, a Baptist minister, who continued to work with Rockefeller on philanthropic projects for 40 years.

During the first decade of the 20th century they established The Rockefeller Institute for Medical Research in 1901, the General Education Board in 1903 and the Rockefeller Sanitary Commission in 1909. The Sanitary Commission became an arm of the International Health Commission and soon all these organizations merged in 1913 to become the Rockefeller Foundation. A group of active trustees, headed by Rockefeller's son, John D. Rockefeller Jr, continued to direct and support all the lines of charitable work that concerned Gates and Rockefeller. The initial financial basis of the Rockefeller Foundation was a gift of 72,569 shares in the Standard Oil Company of New Jersey. The Rockefeller Institute for Medical Research was the first 'Western' establishment devoted entirely to biomedical research, becoming The Rockefeller University in 1965. Earlier, Rockefeller had founded and endowed the University of Chicago.

How the Rockefeller Sanitary Commission came to tackle the hookworm problem remains an intriguing story. In 1902, a zoologist called Dr Charles Wardell Stiles, who happened to be a worm hunter, declared that it was a gross injustice to describe the poor white people of the southern states as indolent and sluggish. Stiles demonstrated that these folk were in the grip of hookworm infection. For the next few years he campaigned fervently to alert authorities to the problem and was often ridiculed by the medical profession. Meanwhile, in 1908, President Theodore Roosevelt appointed Dr Liberty Hyde Bailey, who was Dean of Agriculture at Cornell University, to chair the nation's Country Life Commission. Dr Walter Hines Page served on the Commission and during a tour of the southern states met Stiles who convinced him that something needed to be done about hookworm. Bailey convened a meeting at Cornell University on 16th December 1908, presumably to deal with points in a draft of the Commission's report which was submitted on 21st January 1909. Perhaps Bailey, thanks to the case presented by Page, had by now realized that hookworm was a serious issue. Importantly, Dr Wallace Buttrick, Chairman of the General Education Board, was there and so we may speculate that hookworms eventually came to the attention of that most generous of charities.

The newly formed Sanitary Commission recruited leading biologists and parasitologists to investigate hookworms, the work being co-ordinated by Dr Wickcliffe Rose, a history professor from Tennessee. Shrewdly, Rockefeller judged that, since memories of the Civil War were still alive, a genuine southerner would get better co-operation from the local health boards and their officials than more 'damn Yankees'. The aim of the commission was to bring about the eradication of hookworm disease.

The Commission and then the Foundation adopted a three-phase approach to dealing with hookworms. The first

phase was an epidemiological survey to map the geographical distribution, prevalence and intensity of the infection.
This became a worldwide effort eventually encompassing
52 countries in six continents. The second phase involved
social mobilization, diagnosis by means of stool examination
and then treatment of infected individuals. For most of the
time the available compounds for the expulsion of hookworms were carbon tetrachloride and thymol both of which
were difficult to use and potentially lethal. The severity of
hookworm disease would have been greatly reduced had the
Rockefeller teams had supplies of modern drugs. The third
phase required that sources of contamination were to be lo-
cated and obliterated. That required the universal provision
of sanitation; sadly, 90 years on, far too many people in
hookworm endemic areas still lack sanitation. The Commission's approach to hookworm eradication still applies;
lack of sanitation remains the major problem.

According to former President Jimmy Carter, hookworm was still a public health problem in his home town
in Georgia in the 1930s. He wrote that almost everyone
was afflicted with hookworm from time to time and that
his family avoided hookworm by having a fairly sanitary
outdoor toilet. The developing world is still blighted by
hookworms, but we must note that the Commission's
workers were concerned with dealing with the disease and
not the infection. There is a difference between disease and
infection. One or two hookworms will serve to establish
a case of infection, but many will need to be present for a
person to experience illness or disease. The knowledge
gained between 1909 and the outbreak of World War II

thanks to Rockefeller's philanthropy has been invaluable in helping us understand parasitic disease and how to plan public health interventions for its control.

The commission's southern tour in November 1908 had brought Page in contact with Dr. Charles W. Stiles who had earlier discovered the parasitic cause of hookworm, the intestinal infection that was rampant in the states below the Potomac. ...... Stiles then interjected that the man was simply a victim of hookworm. "Can that man be cured?" asked Page. "About fifty cents worth of drugs will completely cure him," rejoined Stiles.

Reproduced from *Walter Hines Page: The Southerner as American* by John Milton Cooper (1977). Chapel Hill: The University of North Carolina Press.

Sources of Information

Each essay is supported by information that can be traced through the following sources. I have not followed the usual scientific convention of giving details in the text in the hope that readers will go with the flow of what I wanted to say.

CHAPTER ONE: The Prophet of Doom

Bell, P. 1998. *Cities in Civilization*. London: Weidenfeld & Nicolson.
Blackburn, R. 1997. *The Making of New World Slavery*. London and New York: Verso.
Burrow, J. (ed.). 1960. *The Book of Bolton*. Cheltenham and London: J.Burrow & Co. Ltd.
Clarke, A. 1899. *The Effects of the Factory System*. London: Grant Richards. Also published in paperback in 1985 by George Kelsall Publishing, Littleborough, Lancashire.
Europa Publications. 1999. *The Far East and Australasia 1999*. London: Europa Publications Ltd.
Gent, L. 1995. *Bolton Past*. Chichester: Phillimore.
James, L. 1998. *The Rise and Fall of the British Empire*. London: Abacus, Little, Brown and Company (UK).
Office of National Statistics. 1999. Britain 1999. London: The Stationery Office.

Simpson, J A. 1982. *The Concise Dictionary of Proverbs*. London New York Toronto: Oxford University Press.

Stephen, L. (ed.). 1888. *Dictionary of National Biography 13*. London: Smith, Elder & Co. pp.148-150.

CHAPTER TWO: On Brazzaville Beach

Boyd, W. 1990. *Brazzaville Beach*. London: Penguin Books.

Diamond, J. 1992. *The Third Chimpanzee*. HarperCollins*Publishers*. New York.

Downs, R. B. 1956. *Books that Changed the World*. New York and Toronto: The New American Library.

Dugard, M. 2003. *Into Africa*. London: Bantam Press – a Division of Transworld Publishers.

Dunbar, R. I. M. 1988. *Primate Social Systems*. London & Sidney: Croom Helm.

Goodall, J. 1986. *The Chimpanzees of Gombe*. Cambridge, Mass: Bellnap Press of Harvard University.

Stowe, H. B. 1852. *Uncle Tom's Cabin; or Life among the Lowly*. Boston: J.P. Jewett.

Thomas, H. 1997. *The Slave Trade (The History of the Atlantic Slave Trade 1440-1870)*. New York: Simon and Schuster Inc.

CHAPTER THREE: I Didn't Know the Territory

Akogun, O.B. 1989. Parasitic worms in Nigerian folklore. *Parasitology Today* 5, 39.

Amin, M., Willetts, D. & Tetley, B. 1989. *The Beautiful People of*

Kenya. Nairobi, Kenya: Western Sundries Ltd.

Crompton, D. W. T. 1984. *Parasites and People.* Basingstoke and London: Macmillan Publishers Ltd.

Hoeppli, R. 1959. *Parasites and Parasitic Infections in Early Medicine and Science.* Singapore: University of Malaya Press.

Ndeti, K. 1972. *Elements of Akamba Life.* Nairobi, Kenya: East African Publishing House.

Wardlaw, A. C, Forsyth, L. M. G. & Crompton, D. W. T. 1994. Bactericidal activity in the pig roundworm *Ascaris suum.* *Journal of Applied Bacteriology.* 76, 36-41.

CHAPTER FOUR: In Itasca State Park

Ashfall Fossil Beds. State Historical Park, PO Box 66, Royal, NE 68773, USA.

Behbehani, A. M. 1988. *The Smallpox Story.* Kansas City: University of Kansas Medical Center.

Columbia Encyclopedia, 6th edition. 2001 - 2007. New York: Columbia University Press.

Enright, D. J. (ed.).1989. *The Faber Book of Fevers and Frets.* London: Faber and Faber Ltd.

Fenner, F., Henderson, D. A., Arita, I., Jezek, Z. & Ladnyi, I. D. 1988. *Smallpox and its Eradication.* Geneva: World Health Organisation.

Hopkins, D. R. 1983. *Princes and Peasants: Smallpox in History.* Chicago and London: University of Chicago Press.

Janssen, W. F. 1975. America's First Food and Drug Laws. *FDA Consumer* (18 June 1975), 12-18.

Jawetz, E., Melnick, J. L. & Adelberg, E. A. 1980. *Medical Microbiology,* 14th edn. Los Altos, California: Lange Medical Publications.

Knowles, G. 2007. *The Mather Family.* www.controverscial.com.

Middlekauff, R. 1971. *The Mathers: Three Generations of Puritan Intellectuals 1596-1728.* Oxford University Press.

Porter, R. 1997. *The Greatest Benefit to Mankind.* London: HarperCollins *Publishers.*

Royster, P. 2006. An electronic text edition of *A Brief History of the Warr with the Indians in New-England (1676).* University of Nebraska-Lincoln, Faculty Publications, UNL Libraries.

Thomas, H. 1993. *The Conquest of Mexico.* London: Hutchison.

Wellcome Trust. 2006. Did Jesty trump Jenner? *Wellcome News,* Issue 48, October 2006.

WHO. 1980. Smallpox is dead. *World Health*, May, 1980.

CHAPTER FIVE: The Stool of Oosman Kabbia

Crompton, D. W. T. & Savioli, L. 1993. Intestinal parasitic infections and urbanisation. *Bulletin of the World Health Organisation* 71, 1-7.

Entwisle, J. 1848. *A Report of the Sanatory Condition of the Borough of Bolton.* London: Simpkin, Marshall and Co.

Jawetz, E., Melnick, J. L. & Adelberg, E. A. 1980. *Review of Medical Microbiology,* 14th edn. Los Altos, California: Lange Medical Publications.

Seo, B.-S. 1980. Control problem of parasitic infection in Korea. In: *Collected Papers on the Control of Soil-transmitted Helminthiasis, I* (ed. M Yokogawa). Tokyo: Asian Parasite

Control Organization.

UN. 1992. *Long-range World Population Projections.* New York: United Nations.

UNICEF. 2009. *The State of the World's Children.* New York: The United Nations Children's Fund.

CHAPTER SIX: The Number 8 Bus from Cornavin

Bush, K. 2000. Poliomyelitis, war and peace. *Bulletin of the World Health Organisation* 78, 281-282.

Hooper, E. 1999. *The River.* London: Allen Lane, The Penguin Press.

Jamison, D. T. *et al.* 1993. Poliomyelitis. In: *Disease Control Priorities in Developing Countries.* (eds D T Jamison *et al*). Oxford University Press.

Koprowski, H. & Oldstone, M. B. A. 1996. *Microbe Hunters - Then and Now.* Bloomington, Illinois: Medi-Ed Press.

Oates, J. F. 1996. *African Primates. International Union for Conservation of Nature and Natural Resources.* Switzerland: Gland.

Porter, R. 1997. *The Greatest Benefit to Mankind.* London: HarperCollins *Publishers.*

Sleeper, B. & Wolfe, A. 1997. *Primates.* San Francisco: Chronicle Books.

WHO. 1997. *Poliomyelitis: The Beginning of the End.* Geneva: World Health Organisation.

WHO. 2009. The case for completing polio eradication. www.polioeradication.org.

WWF-NL. 1996. Gorilla. IUCN Information Sheets prepared July 1996.

CHAPTER SEVEN: Anemones are my Favourite Flowers

Crompton, D. W. T. 1999. How much human helminthiasis is there in the world? *Journal of Parasitology* 85, 397-403.

Davidson, S., Passmore, R., Brock, J. F. & Truswell, A. S. 1975. *Human Nutrition and Dietetics*, 6th edn. Edinburgh, London and New York: Churchill Livingstone.

Dorland. 1981. *Dorland's Illustrated Medical Dictionary,* 26th edn. Philadelphia and London: W. B. Saunders Company.

Jawetz, E., Melnick, J. L. & Adelburg, E. A. 1980. *Review of Medical Microbiology,* 14th edn. Los Altos, California: Lange Medical Publications.

Nizetic, B. 1975. Public health ophthalmology. In: *The Theory and Practice of Public Health*, 4th edn. (ed. W. Hobson). Oxford University Press, pp 376-399.

Peters, W. & Gilles, H. M. 1989. *A Colour Atlas of Tropical Medicine and Parasitology,* 3rd edn. London: Wolfe Medical Publications Ltd.

Samba, E. M. 1994. *The Onchocerciasis Control Programme in West Africa.* Geneva: World Health Organisation.

Thylefors, B., Negrel, A. D., Pararajasegaram, R. & Dadzie, K. Y. 1995. Global data on blindness. *Bulletin of the World Health Organisation* 73, 115-121.

Vaidyanathan, K, Limburg, H, Foster, A & Pandey, R M. 1999.

Changing trends to barriers in cataract surgery in India. *Bulletin of the World Health Organization* 77, 104-109.

WHO. 2002. *Success in Africa: The Onchocerciasis Programme in West Africa, 1974 – 2002.* Geneva: World Health Organization.

CHAPTER EIGHT: A Cut Above the Rest

Bennett, I. E. 1915. *History of the Panama Canal.* Washington DC: Historical Publishing Company.

Cameron, I. (ed.). 1971. *The Impossible Dream: The Building of the Panama Canal.* London: Hodder and Stoughton.

Doggett, S. 1999. *Panama.* London: Lonely Planet Publications.

Edwards, A. (ed.). 1912. *Panama: The Canal, the Country and the People.* New York: The Macmillan Company.

Evans, M. M. & Reinchenfeld, R. 1998. *Canals of England.* London: Phoenix Illustrated, Orion Publishing Group.

Fleming Brown, I. 1897. Documents in the Archives and Business Records Centre of the University of Glasgow.

Hart, F. R. 1929. *The Disaster of Darien.* Boston and New York: Houghton Mifflin Company.

McCullough, D. 1977. *The Path Between the Seas.* London and New York: Simon & Schuster.

McDonald, D. 1996. *The Clyde Puffer.* Isle of Colonsay, Argyll: House of Lochar.

Panama Canal Information Office. 1980. Notes on the Panama Canal.

Spencer, J. J. 1932. *Catalogue of a Collection of Books and Manuscripts Relating to the Darien Scheme. Glasgow University*

Publications. Glasgow: Jackson, Wylie & Co.

Trevelyan, G.M. 1946. *English Social History,* 2nd Edn. London, New York, Toronto: Longmans, Green and Co.

Watson, M. 1915. *Rural Sanitation in the Tropics.* London: John Murray.

CHAPTER NINE: Yorubaland

Allen, C. 1979. *Tales from the Dark Continent.* London and Sydney: Futura Publications.

Anderson, R. M. & May, R. M. 1991. *Infectious Diseases of Humans.* Oxford University Press.

Cavalli-Sforza, L. & Cavalli-Sforza, F. 1995. *The Great Human Diasporas.* New York and Milan: Addison-Wesley Publishing Company.

Chinweizu. 1988. *Voices from Twentieth-Century Africa.* London and Boston: Faber and Faber.

Holland, C. V. *et al.* 1989. The epidemiology of *Ascaris lumbricoides* and other soil-transmitted helminths in primary school children from Ile-Ife, Nigeria. *Parasitology* 99, 275-285.

Lamb, D. 1985. *The Africans.* London: Methuen London Ltd.

Leakey, R. 1997. The dark continent. In: *Royal Geographical Society Limited.* London, Hong Kong: Scriptum Editions. pp 96-159.

Man, J. 1999. *Atlas of the Year 1000.* London: Penguin Books.

Meredith, M. 2006. *The State of Africa.* London: The Free Press, Simon & Schuster UK Ltd.

Ogunremi, D. & Adediran, B. (eds).1998. *Culture and Society in Yorubaland.* Ibadan, Nigeria: Rex Charles Publications.

Omoleye, B. 1984/85. The origin of the Yoruba - an epitome of controversies. *The African Historian.* 12, 12-19.

CHAPTER TEN: Medicines - Ancient and Modern

Anderson, R. M. & May, R. M. 1991. *Infectious Diseases of Humans.* Oxford University Press.

Clayton, D. H. & Wolfe, N. D. 1993. The adaptive significance of self-medication. *Trends in Evolution and Ecology* 8, 403-408.

Huffman, M. A. 1996. The medicinal use of plants by chimpanzees in the wild. <huffman@macaca.zool.kyoto-u.ac.jp>.

Lederberg, J., Shope, R. E. & Oaks, S. C. 1992. Selective pressure and the development of resistance. In: *Emerging Infections : Microbial Threats to Health in the United States* (eds J. Lederberg, R. E. Shope and S. C. Oaks). USA National Academy Press. pp 92-102.

Le Jambre, L. F., Royal, W. M. & Martin, P. J. 1979. The inheritance of thiabendazole resistance in *Haemonchus contortus. Parasitology* 76, 107-119.

Ou Ming (ed.). 1989. *Chinese-English Manual of Common-used Prescription in Traditional Chinese Medicine.* Hong Kong: Joint Publishing (HK) Co Ltd.

Roos, M. H. *et al.* 1990. Molecular analysis of selection for benzimidazole resistance in the sheep parasite *Haemonchus contortus. Molecular and Biochemical Parasitology* 43, 77-88.

WHO. 1989. *Medicinal Plants in China*. Manila : WHO Regional Office for Western Pacific.

World Bank. 1993. *World Development Report: Investing in Health*. Oxford University Press.

Zhou Xianmin, Peng Weidong & Crompton D.W.T. 1999. Treatment of biliary ascariasis in China. *Transactions of the Royal Society of Tropical Medicine and Hygiene* 93, 561 – 564.

CHAPTER ELEVEN: Off the Road to Mandalay

Christopher, G.W., Cieslak, T.J., Pavlin, J.A. & Eitzen, E.M. 1997. Biological warfare: a historical perspective. *Journal of the American Medical Association* 278, 412-417.

Cowper, J. M. 1957. *The King's Own,* Vol. III. Aldershot: Gale & Polden Ltd.

Eastwood, S. 1991. *Lions of England*. Kettering, Northants: Silver Link Publishing.

Ellis, J. 1993. *The Sharp End*. London: Pimlico.

Harrison, G. 1978. *Mosquitoes, Malaria and Man*. London: John Murray.

Hutton, J. 2008. *Kitchener's Men. The King's Own Royal Lancasters on the Western Front 1915 – 1918*. Barnsley, Yorkshire: Pen & Sword Military.

McGregor, I. A. 1996. Malaria. In: *The Wellcome Trust Illustrated History of Tropical Disease* (ed. F E G Cox). London: The Welcome Trust. pp 230-247.

Najera, J. A., Kouznetzsov, R. L. & Delacollette, C. 1998. *Malaria Epidemics*. Geneva: World Health Organisation. (WHO/MAL/ 98.1084)

Roberts, L. S. & Janovy, J. 1996. *Foundations of Parasitology,* 5th edn. London: Wm C. Brown, Publishers.

Thomson, J. 1998. *War Behind Enemy Lines.* London: Sidgwick & Jackson with the Imperial War Museum.

Working Group on Global Parasite Control. 1998. *The Global Parasite Control for the 21st Century.* Government of Japan.

CHAPTER TWELVE: Advice from Uncle Azael

Ardayfio-Schandorf, E. 1993. Household energy supply and women's work in Ghana. In: *Different Places, Different Voices* (eds J. H. Momsen and V. Kinnard). London: Routledge. pp 15 - 29.

Ayensu, E. S., Heywood, V. H., Lucas, G. L. & Defilipps, R. A. 1984. *Our Green and Living World.* Cambridge University Press.

Beazley, M. (ed.). 1982. *The Atlas of Mankind.* London: Mitchell Beazley Publishers.

Bishop, P. 1999. *100 Woods.* Marlborough, Wiltshire: The Crowood Press Ltd.

BM(NH). 1959. *A Handbook on Evolution.* London: Trustees of the British Museum.

Groombridge, B. (ed.).1992. *Global Biodiversity.* London and Glasgow: Chapman and Hall.

Morrell, V. 2000. Blue Nile. *National Geographic.* December 2000, 2 - 29.

Schimper, A. F. W. 1903. *Plant-geography upon a Physiological Basis.* (eds P. Groom and I. B. Balfour). Oxford University Press. [Translated from the German by W. R. Fisher.]

Simberloff, D. 1986. Are we on the verge of mass extinction in tropical rain forests? In: *Dynamics of Extinction* (ed. D. K. Elliott). New York: John Wiley. pp.165-180.

CHAPTER THIRTEEN: From Richford to Riches

Chernow, R. 1999. *The Life of John D. Rockefeller, Sr.* New York: Vintage Books.

Crompton, D. W. T. & Whitehead, R. R. 1993. Hookworm infections and human iron metabolism. *Parasitology* 107, S137-S145.

Ettling, J. 1990. The role of The Rockefeller Foundation in hookworm research and control. In: *Hookworm Disease* (eds G. A. Schad and K. S. Warren). London and Philadelphia: Taylor & Francis Ltd. pp. 3-14.

Financial Times, Wednesday 5 April 2000.

Fosdick, R. B. 1989. *The Story of the Rockefeller Foundation.* New Brunswick and Oxford: Transaction Publishers.

Garraty, J. A. & Carnes, M. C. (eds). 1999. *American National Bibliography 18.* Oxford University Press.

Haldane, J. S. 1903. Report to the Secretary of State for the Home Department on Ankylostomiasis in Westphalian Collieries. Presented to both Houses of Parliament by Command of His Majesty. London: HMSO.

Pawlowski, Z. S., Schad, G. A. & Stott, G. J. 1991. *Hookworm Infection and Anaemia.* Geneva: World Health Organization.

Rubenstein, W. & Beresford, P. 2000. Richest of the rich. In: *The Sunday Times,* 26th March 2000.

Chapter Drawings

On Becoming a Worm Hunter
Freshwater shrimp (*Gammarus*) that serves as intermediate host
for *Polymorphus* an intestinal worm found in waterfowl.

CHAPTER ONE: The Prophet of Doom
Proboscis of a thorny-headed worm (*Acanthocephalus*) from the
intestine of an eel.

CHAPTER TWO: On Brazzaville Beach
Cuckoo (*Cuculus*) whose habit of brood parasitism was discovered by Edward Jenner, the pioneer of vaccination.

CHAPTER THREE: I Didn't Know the Territory
Adult whipworm (*Trichuris*) from the rectal lining of a child.

CHAPTER FOUR: In Itasca State Park
Cysticercoid of a tapeworm (*Hymenolepis*) that will infect and
mature in a rat.

CHAPTER FIVE: The Stool of Oosman Kabbia
Adult male blood fluke (*Schistosoma*) cradling its female partner.
These flukes cause Bilharzia or schistosomiasis in millions of
people.

CHAPTER SIX: The Number 8 Bus from Cornavin

Eggs of roundworm (*Ascaris*, top), hookworm (*Necator*, middle) and whipworm (*Trichuris,* bottom), pathogenic agents of intestinal infections in millions of people.

CHAPTER SEVEN: Anemones are my Favourite Flowers

Activated acanthocephalan cystacanth from which the proboscis has emerged to grip the intestinal wall of its host.

CHAPTER EIGHT: A Cut Above the Rest

Freshwater leech (*Hemiclepsis*) that serves as intermediate host for an intestinal fluke found in ducks.

CHAPTER NINE: Yorubaland

Eggs of blood flukes (*Schistosoma mansoni*, top and *S. haematobium,* bottom) responsible for severe tissue damage in infected people.

CHAPTER TEN: Medicines – Ancient and Modern

Adult Chinese liver fluke (*Opisthorchis)*, a highly pathogenic and carcinogenic parasite of millions of people.

CHAPTER ELEVEN: Off the Road to Mandalay

Body of an adult tapeworm made up of segments or proglottides.

CHAPTER TWELVE: Advice from Uncle Azael

Head, with lips around the mouth, of a roundworm (*Ascaris*) from a pig.

CHAPTER THIRTEEN: From Richford to Riches

Acanthor of a thorny-headed worm (*Moniliformis*) which invades the body cavity of a cockroach.

> "... and so there ain't nothing more to write about, and I am rotten glad of it, because if I'd 'a' knowed what a trouble it was to make a book I wouldn't 'a' tackled it, and ain't a-going to no more."

From *The Adventures of Huckleberry Finn* by Mark Twain (1884). Cleveland and New York: The World Publishing Company (1947).

The Glasgow Centre for International Development

The Glasgow Centre for International Development (GCID) is an interdisciplinary research centre at the University of Glasgow which has the responsibility for co-ordinating the University's research and training activities in the field of international development. This involves almost 100 academic and research staff from across the University, almost all of whom are actively involved in collaborative research with colleagues in Africa and Asia. GCID has four main areas of research activity: Human and Animal Health; Environmental Management; Education, Lifelong Learning and Gobal Citizenship; and Economic Development. If you are interested in more information, please visit our website at www.gla.ac.uk/gcid

One of GCID's main aims is to promote research capacity building in some of the world's poorest countries, most of which are in sub-Saharan Africa. Central to supporting this is the GCID Scholarship Scheme which is designed to support the research training of high-achieving candidates, with successful students spending at least one year out of three conducting research back in their own country. It is also a requirement that the topic of their research is of direct development relevance to the home country.

We are delighted that the proceeds from the sale of this book will go directly into the GCID Scholarship Scheme fund, so contributing to the solution of some of the most pressing development challenges of some of the poorest countries in the world.

Further copies of the book may be obtained from the following address, with cheques being made payable to 'University of Glasgow':

Professor John Briggs
Director
Glasgow Centre for International Development
East Quadrangle
University of Glasgow
Glasgow
G12 8QQ
United Kingdom

If you would like to make further contributions to the GCID Scholarship Scheme fund, please feel free to contact us at gcidadmin@gla.ac.uk or write to us at the address above.